THE CHARLTON PRICE GUIDE TO

BESWICK ANIMALS

First Edition

MW00364843

By

Diana Callow
John Callow

Marilyn Sweet
Peter Sweet

Publisher
W. K. Cross

The Charlton Press

Toronto, Ontario ❖ Birmingham, Michigan

COPYRIGHT NOTICE AND TRADEMARK NOTICE

Copyright © 1994 Charlton International Inc. All Rights Reserved

Photographs © Charlton International Inc.

The terms Charlton, Charlton's, The Charlton Press and abbreviations thereof, are trademarks of Charlton International Inc. and shall not be used without written consent from Charlton International Inc.

The words Doulton and Royal Doulton are a registered trade mark of Royal Doulton (UK) Limited and are used herein to express items of collector interest.

While every care has been taken to ensure accuracy in the compilation of the data in this catalogue, the publisher cannot accept responsibility for typographical errors.

No part of this publication, except the various numbering systems, may be reproduced, stored in a retrieval system, or transmitted in any form or by any means, electronic, mechanical, photocopying, recording, or otherwise, without the prior written permission of the copyright owner.

No copyright material may be used without written permission in each instance from Charlton International Inc. Permission is hereby given for brief excerpts to be used in newspapers, magazines, periodicals and bulletins, other than in the advertising of items for sale, providing the source of the material so used is acknowledged in each instance.

DISCLAIMER

Products listed or shown were manufactured by Royal Doulton (UK) Limited. This book has been produced independently and neither the authors nor the publisher has any connection whatsoever with either Royal Doulton (UK) Limited or the Royal Doulton International Collectors Club. Royal Doulton is a registered trade mark and is used in this book with the permission of Royal Doulton (UK) Limited. Any opinions expressed are those of the authors and not necessarily endorsed by Royal Doulton (UK) Limited.

Canadian Cataloguing In Publication Data
Main entry under title:
The Charlton price guide to Beswick animals
1995-
Biennial.
ISSN
ISBN 0-88968-14-0 (1st ed.)
1. Royal Doulton figurines--Catalogues
2. Porcelain animals--Catalogues
3. Royal Doulton animals - Catalogue

**Printed in Canada
in the Province of Quebec**

The Charlton Press

**Editorial Office
2010 Yonge Street
Toronto, Canada. M4S 1Z9
Telephone (416) 488-4653 Fax: (416) 488-4656**

EDITORIAL

Editor	Jean Dale
Layout	Marc Rowan
Proofing	Frank van Lieshout

ACKNOWLEDGMENTS

The Charlton Press wishes to thank those who have helped and assisted with the first edition of the Charlton Price Guide to Beswick Animals.

SPECIAL THANKS

Our thanks also go to The Beswick Collectors Circle, Royal Doulton (U.K.) Limited, Royal Doulton (Canada) Ltd. and Royal Doulton USA Inc. who helped with additional technical information and photography.

CONTRIBUTORS

The Publisher would like to thank the following individuals or companies who graciously supplied photographs or allowed us access to their collections for photographic purposes. We offer sincere thanks to:

Julie Allen, Helen Carter, Fred Deardon, Allan and Lorraine Green, Edna Holland, Chris Lane, Val and Bryan Leach, Nick Sales.

A SPECIAL NOTE TO COLLECTORS

We welcome and appreciate any comments or suggestions in regard to the Charlton Price Guide to Beswick Animals. If you would like to participate in pricing or supply previously unavailable data or information, please contact Jean Dale at (416) 488-4653.

BESWICK
Connoisseur Range
COLLECTORS PIECES

HUNTER. 1734/9801—11¼"
Magnificent example of a Hunter

RACEHORSE 1564/9800—11½"
Attractive model of a Racehorse

XAYAL. 1265/9807—6¼"
From the Arab XAYAL, now at stud in SIAM

ARKLE. 2065/9790—11" Winner of the Cheltenham Gold Cup three consecutive years. His achievements and remarkable qualities make him the greatest steeplechaser of all time. Owned by Anne, Duchess of Westminster and trained by Tom Dreaper in Ireland

ARKLE. 2084/9802—12¾"
With Ireland's famous jockey Pat Taaffe

HEREFORD BULL. 1363/9805—4¾"
Modelled to the standard of the Hereford Cattle Society

THOROUGHBRED. 1772/9800
8" The Thoroughbred is the best known British breed

ARAB. 1771/9801—7½"
One of the oldest and most beautiful breeds

FRIESIAN BULL. 1439—4¾" Modelled from Champion "Coddington Hilt Bar"

BEAGLE. 1931/9804—6"
Modelled from Champion Wendover Billy

BASSETT. 2045/9803—5"
Modelled from Champion Fochno Trinket

JOHN BESWICK LTD., Gold Street, Longton, Stoke-on-Trent, ST3 2JP, England
Telephone Stoke-on-Trent 33041   Cables Beswara, Stoke-on-Trent

A MEMBER OF THE ROYAL DOULTON GROUP OF COMPANIES

TABLE OF CONTENTS

A FLOW CHART FOR THE MAKING OF A BESWICK HORSE

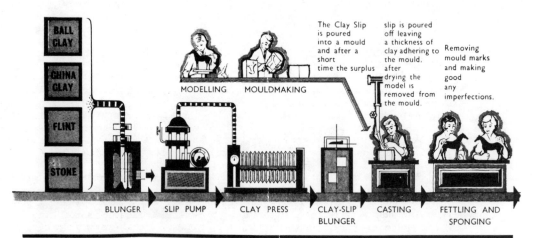

BALL CLAY

CHINA CLAY

FLINT

STONE

MODELLING   MOULDMAKING

The Clay Slip is poured into a mould and after a short time the surplus

slip is poured off leaving a thickness of clay adhering to the mould, after drying the model is removed from the mould.

Removing mould marks and making good any imperfections.

BLUNGER   SLIP PUMP   CLAY PRESS   CLAY-SLIP BLUNGER   CASTING   FETTLING AND SPONGING

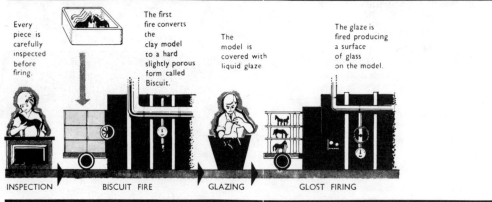

Every piece is carefully inspected before firing.

The first fire converts the clay model to a hard slightly porous form called Biscuit.

The model is covered with liquid glaze

The glaze is fired producing a surface of glass on the model.

INSPECTION   BISCUIT FIRE   GLAZING   GLOST FIRING

Artists applying colour

The colour is fired on to the glaze.

Final inspection before packing.

DECORATING   DECORATING FIRING   INSPECTION   PACKING   TRANSPORTATION

INTRODUCTION

An article entitled "Equestrian Figures for Collectors —Growth of the House of Beswick," in the *Pottery Gazette and Glass Trade Review* of September 1961, ended with this paragraph: "Among the potters of the present day yet to reach the one hundred-year mark, and whose products are already highly prized, none is more likely to be of future interest to collectors and antique dealers than the House of Beswick." How prophetic this has proved to be. In 1985 the Beswick Collector's Circle was formed as interest in the products of the Beswick factory was aroused. The circle has flourished as more and more people worldwide have joined the search to add to their collections and to seek information in order to enjoy their finds to the full. This book represents the most comprehensive attempt to date to form as complete a guide as possible to the Beswick animal collection.

In 1994 the John Beswick factory celebrated its centenary—a hundred years of producing an unbelievably wide variety of pottery items, from mundane household earthenware right through to the intricate ornamental ware and pure ornaments of all shapes and sizes.

Initially the factory produced plain and decorated ware. An advertisement from about 1900 lists "jugs, tea ware, dinner ware, toilet ware, flower pots, pedestals, novelties, vases, figures, bread trays, cheese dishes, etc., etc." The figures included the traditional Old Staffordshire dogs, but hares and hounds, horses, generals, a cow and calf, milkmaids, gardeners and Puss in Boots are also mentioned. Unfortunately many of these pieces were not marked Beswick.

From the start the Beswick factory was very much a family-run firm. James Wright Beswick, the founder, and his sons, John and Gilbert, and John's son, John Ewart, were all very committed to the factory's success. In 1934 ,when John Ewart Beswick became chairman and managing director and his uncle, Gilbert Beswick, was sales manager, several new pieces were introduced to the range, and recorded in the "shape book."

Arthur Gredington in his studio

This was the start of shape numbers being impressed into the base whenever possible and also the more widespread use of a Beswick backstamp.

Five years later Arthur Gredington took up his appointment as the first full-time modeller. His influence was enormous, for he had a great talent for modelling not only accurate and realistic animals of all kinds, but also ones of the comical variety, for example the very appealing "Grebie," number 1006. Consequently his name appears more than that of any other person in this book, and it is a tribute to his skill that many of his models are still in production in 1995 as *Doulton Animals*.

James Hayward also made an outstanding contribution to the high quality associated with the Beswick name. As decorating manager from 1934 and art director from 1957, he was responsible for designing almost three thousand different decorations and patterns. He also designed new shapes, such as the 720 "Panda Cub," and was an outstanding glaze chemist. His experience with glazes was fundamental in the development of the matt glaze used initially on the top of the range *Connoisseur Series*.

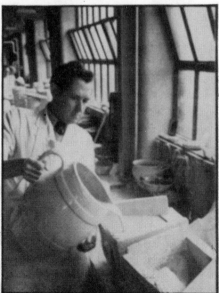

Mould making

When a complex model, such as an animal, is being manufactured, the mould it will be produced from is of vital importance. In this department Albert Hallam had exceptional skill. He joined Beswick in 1926 at age 14 as an apprentice mouldmaker and went on to become head of the mouldmaking department and also a modeller. The series of butterflies are Albert Hallam's creations, as are a number of horses, dogs and cats, which were modelled after Arthur Gredington's retirement. These include at least one model that is very sought after today, number 2282 "Norwegian Fjord Horse."

There are several other modellers whose work is featured in this book. Very little is known about some of them as they tended to be employed on a freelance basis, for example, Miss Catford, who modelled character-type animals like the 663 "Elephant" holding a five-ton weight and Mr. Garbet, who contributed cats, dogs and a sheep. Although small in number, significant contributions were also made by Alan Maslankowski, whose 2578 "Shire Horse" is quite magnificent, Colin Melbourne, who besides the unique "*C.M.*" *Series* also modelled most of the Peter Scott ducks, Graham Orwell whose models included the 1374 "Galloping Horse" and 1391 "Mounted Indian," and Pal Zalman whose one equine model, the 1549 "Head tucked Horse," is still in production.

By the late 1960s, Ewart and Gilbert Beswick were nearing retirement, and as there was not another generation to follow them into the family business, the decision was made in 1969 to sell to Royal Doulton. Beswick animals continued to be produced, and although much rationalization took place, such as reducing the number of colourways of the horses and withdrawing many pieces, the ranges were also expanded by the regular introduction of new pieces.

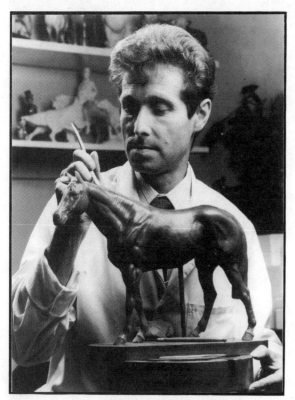

Graham Tongue at work

Then in August 1989, the decision was implemented to make the vast majority of the remaining animals produced at the Beswick factory into *Doulton Animals* , and the pieces were all issued with DA numbers. At the same time, grey and palomino matts were withdrawn from the horses' colourways, and only a few continued to be available in grey and palomino glosses.

Currently the modelling team at Beswick is headed by design manager Graham Tongue and includes the young team of Warren Platt, Amanda Hughes-Lubeck and Martyn Alcock. Graham Tongue has worked at Beswick since 1966 and became head modeller in 1973, when Albert Hallam retired. He has concentrated on the modelling of animals, and his modelling skill is apparent in almost all the sections here.

Graham Tongue has the distinction of modelling the piece which holds the world-record price for a piece of Beswick, appropriately an equine model entitled the "Spirit of Whitfield." In 1987 he was commissioned by the Chatterley Mining Museum to model Kruger, the last pit pony used at the Staffordshire mine. The resulting model, based on the 2541 "Welsh Mountain Pony," was considerably adapted with incredible attention to detail. The result was superb. Only four models were made, one each for the Beswick and Chatterley Whitfield museums, one presented to HRH Princess Anne when she visited the museum, and one was auctioned in aid of the Princess's favourite charity. In April 1994 the mining museum was closed and everything was auctioned. The "Spirit of Whitfield" sold for £2,750, a far cry from one hundred years ago when Beswick was advertising pieces for 6 1/2d.

Although very few animals now carry the Beswick backstamp, this book illustrates the animal kingdom as seen through the eyes of the Beswick designers since the early 1930s. Cats and kittens with appealing eyes, birds and butterflies to fly across walls, a well-stocked zoo with animals from all over the world, everyday farm animals, animals which make you laugh, champion dogs, sleek horses and fish leaping from their pools are all lasting reminders of the Beswick story. The story will continue as more information emerges and the elusive models are discovered.

THE BESWICK COLLECTORS CIRCLE

After ten years as coordinators of the Beswick Collectors Circle, John and Diana Callow have, for mainly personal reasons, decided to retire. The B.C.C. will close in 1995 with an anniversary weekend in October and a special anniversary newsletter in November. Many thanks to John and Diana for their tireless efforts that made the B.C.C.

Collectors who are interested in joining a Beswick Guild/Society/Club should contact Marilyn Sweet at:

Lochinver, 21 Lymbridge Drive, Blackrod,
Bolton, Lancashire, England. BL6 5TH

LABELS AND BACKSTAMPS

gummed seal
which is
affixed to
Figures and
Vases wherever
possible

BESWICK
ENGLAND

BESWICK
·ENGLAND·

BESWICK ENGLAND

Illustrating a
trademark which
is impressed in
the mould
beneath a wide
range of
productions

Backstamps which are printed underneath the ware, wherever practicable

A NOTE ON PRICING

In addition to providing accurate information, this catalogue gives readers the most up-to-date retail prices for Beswick animal figures in American, Canadian and British currencies.

To accomplish this, The Charlton Press continues to access an international pricing panel of Beswick experts that submits prices based on both dealer and collector retail price activity as well as current auction results in the U.S., Canadian and U.K. markets. These market prices are carefully analysed and adjusted to reflect accurate valuations for the listed Beswick animal figures in each of these three markets.

Please be aware that all prices given in a particular currency are for figures within that particular country. The prices published herein have not been calculated using exchange rates exclusively. They have been determined solely by supply and demand within the country in question.

A necessary word of caution. No pricing catalogue can be, or should be, a fixed price list. This catalogue, therefore, should be considered as a pricing guide only - showing the most current retail prices based on market demand within a particular region for the various figures.

Current figures, however, are priced differently in this catalogue. Such pieces are priced according to the manufacturer's suggested retail price in each of the three market regions. Be aware that dealer discounting is always possible.

Prices published herein are for figures in mint condition. Collectors are cautioned that a repaired or restored piece may be worth as little as 50 per cent of the value of the same figure in mint condition. The collector interested strictly in investment potential will avoid damaged or restored figurines.

As mentioned above, this is a catalogue giving prices for figures in the currency of three particular markets (Canadian dollars for the Canadian markets; U.S. dollars for the American market and Sterling for the U.K. market.) The bulk of the prices given herein are not determined by straight currency exchange calculations but by actual market activity in the market concerned. This point bears repeating.

One exception, however, occurs in the case of current figurines and very recent limited editions issued in only one of the three markets. Since such items were priced by Royal Doulton only in the country in which they were to be sold, prices for the other countries have been shown as N/A (not applicable).

Additionally, collectors must remember that all relevant information must be known to make a proper valuation. When comparing auction prices to catalogue prices, collectors and dealers must remember two important points.

Firstly, to compare 'apples and apples'. Be sure that realized auction prices for figures include a buyer's premium if one is due. Prices realized for figures in auction catalogues may not include this additional amount. Buyer's premium can range from 10% to 15% and on an expensive piece this amount can be significant. Secondly, if a figure is restored or repaired, this fact may not be noted or explained anywhere in the listings and as a result, its price will not be reflective of that same piece in mint condition. Please be aware of repairs and restorations and the effect they may have on published figure values.

Welcome to the world of BESWICK

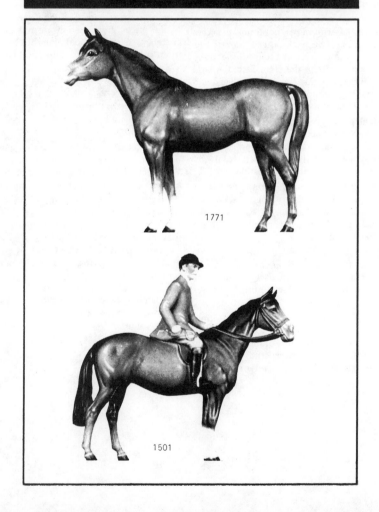

1771

1501

Chapter One

BIRDS

The models of our "feathered friends" are a delight for any bird enthusiast, and there are plenty here to choose from.

They come in all sizes, from very small birds, such as the little wren, to the impressive and large pheasant from the *Connoisseur Series* . Some are expensive, some are not, and quite a few are still in production. The figures cover a wide range from the comic *Fun Models* to wall plaques to the precise realism of the *Peter Scott Wildfowl* collection. When displayed in groups, the colours of their plumage create an impressive display.

Among the birds in this group are species that you could see any day of the week in your garden and also more exotic or rare varieties, such as the toucan, bald eagle, penguin and kookaburra.

INDEX BY MODEL NUMBER

Model No. 317
DUCK - On pottery base

Designer:	Miss Greaves
Height:	8 1/4", 21.0 cm
Colours:	Yellow duck with brown feet and beak, blue base - gloss
Issued:	c.1936-1954
Series:	Fun Models

Description:	U.K. £	U.S. $	Can. $
Gloss	95.00	150.00	200.00

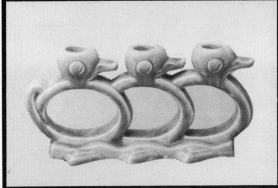

Model No. 370
DUCKS - Candleholder

Designer:	J. Hayward
Height:	3 1/2", 8.9 cm
Colours:	Brown with blue - gloss
Issued:	1935-By 1954

Description:	U.K. £	U.S. $	Can. $
Gloss	45.00	70.00	100.00

Model No. 450
PENGUIN

Designer:	Mr. Owen
Height:	Large - 8", 20.3 cm
	Small - 3 1/2", 8.9 cm
Colours:	1: Black and white - gloss
	2: Blue - gloss
Issued:	1936-By 1954

Description:	U.K. £	U.S. $	Can. $
1: Large - black	95.00	150.00	300.00
1: Small - black	65.00	100.00	200.00
2: Large - blue	95.00	150.00	300.00
2: Small - blue	65.00	100.00	200.00

Model No. 497
PELICAN - Matchbox holder

Designer:	Mr. Watkin
Height:	4", 10.1 cm
Colours:	Green, white and brown - gloss
Issued:	1937-1955

Description:	U.K. £	U.S. $	Can. $
Gloss	75.00	95.00	170.00

Model No. 617
DUCK - Ashtray

Designer:	Mr. Watkin
Height:	3", 7.6 cm
Colours:	1: Greens and oranges
	2: Blue
Issued:	1938-By 1954

Description:	U.K. £	U.S. $	Can. $
1: Green/orange	95.00	150.00	200.00
2: Blue	95.00	150.00	200.00

Model No. 618
PUFFIN

Designer:	Mr. Owen
Height:	9", 22.9 cm
Colours:	Blue - gloss
Issued:	1938-By 1954

Description:	U.K. £	U.S. $	Can. $
Gloss	110.00	175.00	250.00

Model No. 749
MALLARD DUCK - Rising

Designer:	Arthur Gredington
Height:	6 1/2", 16.5 cm
Colours:	Browns, teal green and white - gloss
Issued:	1939-By 1965

Description:	U.K. £	U.S. $	Can. $
Gloss	125.00	200.00	275.00

Model No. 750
MALLARD DUCK - Settling

Designer:	Arthur Gredington
Height:	6 1/2", 16.5 cm
Colours:	Browns, teal green and white - gloss
Issued:	1939-By 1965

Description:	U.K. £	U.S. $	Can. $
Gloss	110.00	175.00	275.00

Model No. 754
PHEASANT - Ashtray

Designer:	Mr. Watkin
Height:	3 1/2", 8.9 cm
Colours:	Teal green and brown - gloss
Issued:	1939-1971

Description:	U.K. £	U.S. $	Can. $
Gloss	45.00	70.00	100.00

Note: Model no. 767A was used.

Model No. 755
DUCK - Ashtray

Designer:	Mr. Watkin
Height:	4", 10.1 cm
Colours:	Teal green, brown and white - gloss
Issued:	1939-1969

Description:	U.K. £	U.S. $	Can. $
	45.00	70.00	100.00

Note: Model no. 756/3 was used.

Model No. 756
MALLARD DUCK - Standing

Designer:	Mr. Watkin
Height:	756/1 - 7", 17.8 cm
	756/2 - 5 3/4", 14.6 cm
	756/2A - 4 1/2", 11.9 cm
	756/3 - 3 1/2", 8.9 cm
Colours:	1: Brown, teal green and white - gloss
	2: Blue - gloss
Issued:	1939-1973

Description:		U.K. £	U.S. $	Can. $
756/1	Brown	65.00	100.00	150.00
756/1	Blue	65.00	100.00	150.00
756/2	Brown	55.00	85.00	125.00
756/2	Blue	55.00	85.00	125.00
756/2A	Brown	55.00	85.00	125.00
756/2A	Blue	55.00	85.00	125.00
756/3	Brown	45.00	70.00	100.00
756/3	Blue	45.00	70.00	100.00

Note: Model no. 756/3 has grass around feet.
Model no. 902 makes a set of five pieces.

Model No. 760
DUCK WITH LADYBIRD ON BEAK

Designer: Mr. Watkin
Height: 3 3/4", 9.5 cm
Colours: White with yellow beak,
               ladybird on beak - gloss
Issued: 1939-1971
Series: Fun Models

Description:	U.K. £	U.S. $	Can. $
Gloss	65.00	100.00	145.00

Model No. 762
DUCK ON SKIS

Designer: Mr. Watkin
Height: 3 1/4", 8.3 cm
Colours: White with orange beak - gloss
Issued: 1939-1969
Series: Fun Models

Description:	U.K. £	U.S. $	Can. $
Gloss	65.00	100.00	145.00

Model No. 765
DUCK FAMILY

Designer: Arthur Gredington
Height: 2 3/4" x 7", 7.0 x 17.8 cm
Colours: White with yellow beaks - gloss
Issued: 1939-1971

Description:	U.K. £	U.S. $	Can. $
Gloss	45.00	70.00	100.00

Model No. 767A
PHEASANT
Version One - Curved tail

Designer: Mr. Watkin
Height: 3", 7.6 cm
Colours: Red brown, teal green - gloss
Issued: Gloss: 1939-1971

Description:	U.K. £	U.S. $	Can. $
Gloss	45.00	70.00	100.00

Note: This model was used on 754 (pheasant ashtray).

Photograph not
available at press time

Model No. 767B
PHEASANT
Version Two - Straight tail

Designer: Mr. Watkin
Height: 3", 7.6 cm
Colours: Red, brown and teal green - gloss or matt
Issued: 1: Gloss - 1971-1995
              2: Matt - 1983-1989

Description:	U.K. £	U.S . $	Can. $
1: Gloss	10.00	15.00	20.00
2: Matt	15.00	25.00	30.00

Model No. 768
SEAGULL ON ROCK

Designer: Arthur Gredington
Height: 8 1/2", 21.6 cm
Colours: Cream and dark brown,
              green and yellow base - gloss
Issued: 1939-By 1954

Description:	U.K. £	U.S. $	Can. $
Gloss	195.00	300.00	425.00

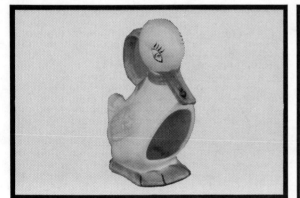

Model No. 769
DUCK - Night light holder

Designer: Mr. Watkin
Height: 6", 20.3 cm
Colours: Yellow and white, orange beak - gloss
Issued: 1939-By 1954

Description:	U.K. £	U.S. $	Can. $
Gloss		Rare	

Model No. 800
PENGUIN - Chick

Designer: Arthur Gredington
Height: 2", 5.0 cm
Colours: Black and white with
              yellow markings- gloss
Issued: 1940-1973
Set: 801, 802, 803

Description:	U.K. £	U.S. $	Can. $
Gloss	25.00	40.00	55.00

Model No. 801
PENGUIN - Chick

Designer:	Arthur Gredington
Height:	2", 5.0 cm
Colours:	Black and white with yellow markings - gloss
Issued:	1940-1973
Set:	800, 802, 803

Description:	U.K. £	U.S. $	Can. $
Gloss	25.00	40.00	55.00

Model No. 802
PENGUIN - With umbrella

Designer:	Arthur Gredington
Height:	4 1/4", 10.8 cm
Colours:	1: Black and white, red umbrella - gloss
	2: Black and white, green umbrella - gloss
Issued:	1940-1973
Set:	800, 801, 803

Description:	U.K. £	U.S. $	Can. $
1: Red umbrella	50.00	95.00	160.00
2: Green umbrella	75.00	125.00	200.00

Note: Model 802 was altered in 1956.

Model No. 803
PENGUIN - With walking stick

Designer:	Arthur Gredington
Height:	3 3/4", 9.5 cm
Colours:	Black and white with yellow markings, black walking stick - gloss
Issued:	1940-1973
Set:	800, 801, 802

Description:	U.K. £	U.S. $	Can. $
Gloss	35.00	65.00	100.00

Note: Model 802 was altered in 1956.

Photograph not
available at press time

Model No. 817/1
MALLARD DUCK - Squatting

Designer:	Mr. Watkin
Height:	7 1/2", 19.1 cm
Colours:	Brown, teal green and white - gloss
Issued:	1940-1954
Set:	817/2

Description::	U.K. £	U.S. $	Can. $
Gloss	110.00	175.00	250.00

Model No. 817/2
MALLARD DUCK - Squatting

Designer:	Mr. Watkin		
Height:	6 3/4", 17.2 cm		
Colours:	Brown, teal green and white - gloss		
Issued:	1940-1970		
Set:	817/1		

Description:	*U.K. £*	*U.S. $*	*Can. $*
Gloss	95.00	150.00	200.00

Model No. 820
GEESE (Pair)

Designer:	Arthur Gredington		
Height:	4", 10.1 cm		
Colours:	White with orange feet and beaks - gloss		
Issued:	1940-1971		
Series:	Fun Models		
Set:	821, 822		

Description:	*U.K. £*	*U.S. $*	*Can. $*
Gloss	45.00	70.00	100.00

Model No. 821
GOSLING - Facing left

Designer:	Arthur Gredington		
Height:	2 1/4", 5.7 cm		
Colours:	White with orange beak - gloss		
Issued:	1940-1971		
Series:	Fun Models		
Set:	820, 822		

Description:	*U.K. £*	*U.S. $*	*Can. $*
Gloss	35.00	55.00	75.00

Model No. 822
GOSLING - Facing right

Designer:	Arthur Gredington		
Height:	1 3/4", 4.3 cm		
Colours:	White with orange beak - gloss		
Issued:	1940-1971		
Series:	Fun Models		
Set:	820, 821		

Description:	*U.K. £*	*U.S. $*	*Can. $*
Gloss	30.00	55.00	75.00

Model No. 827
DUCK - Standing

Designer:	Mr. Watkin
Height:	Large - 7 1/2", 19.1 cm
	Medium - 6", 15.0 cm
	Small - 5", 12.7 cm
Colours:	White, brown and yellow - gloss
Issued:	1940-By 1954

Description:	U.K. £	U.S. $	Can. $
Large	95.00	150.00	225.00
Medium	85.00	135.00	190.00
Small	75.00	120.00	165.00

Model No. 849
PHEASANT ON BASE - Flying upwards

Designer:	Arthur Gredington
Height:	6", 15.0 cm
Colours:	Browns, teal green and yellow - gloss
Issued:	1940-1971

Description:	U.K. £	U.S. $	Can. $
Gloss	110.00	175.00	250.00

Model No. 850
PHEASANT ON BASE - Settling

Designer:	Arthur Gredington
Height:	5 3/4", 14.6 cm
Colours:	Browns, teal green and yellow - gloss
Issued:	1940-1971

Description:	U.K. £	U.S. $	Can. $
Gloss	100.00	150.00	225.00

Photograph not
available at press time

Model No. 862
BIRD

Designer: Miss Joachin
Height: Unknown
Colours: Unknown
Issued: 1940-Unknown

Description:	U.K. £	U.S. $	Can. $
	Extremely Rare		

Note: Possibly not produced.

Model No. 902
MALLARD DUCK - Standing

Designer: Arthur Gredington
Height: 10", 25.4 cm
Colours: 1: Brown and teal green - gloss
2: Brown, teal green or white - gloss
Issued: 1940-1970

Description:	U.K. £	U.S. $	Can. $
1: Brown	125.00	200.00	275.00
2: Brown/white	125.00	200.00	275.00

Note: Makes a set of five with 756/1, 756/2, 756/2A, 756/3

Model No. 919A
DUCK - Large

Designer: Mr. Watkin
Height: 3 3/4", 9.5 cm
Colours: Brown, teal green, white and pink - gloss
Issued: 1941-1971

Description:	U.K. £	U.S. $	Can. $
Gloss	45.00	70.00	100.00

Model No. 919B
DUCK - Medium

Designer: Mr. Watkin
Height: 2 1/2", 6.4 cm
Colours: Brown, teal green, white and pink - gloss
Issued: 1941-1971

Description:	U.K. £	U.S. $	Can. $
Gloss	30.00	50.00	65.00

Model No. 919C
DUCK - Small

Designer: Mr. Watkin
Height: 2", 5.0 cm
Colours: Brown, teal green, white and pink - gloss
Issued: 1941-1971

Description:	U.K. £	U.S. $	Can. $
Gloss	25.00	40.00	55.00

Model No. 925
AMERICAN BLUE JAYS

Designer: Arthur Gredington
Height: 5", 12.7 cm
Colours: Blue - gloss
Issued: 1941-By 1965

Description:	U.K. £	U.S. $	Can. $
Gloss	110.00	175.00	250.00

Model No. 926
BALTIMORE ORIOLES

Designer: Arthur Gredington
Height: 5", 12.7 cm
Colours: Golden and dark brown with blue markings - gloss
Issued: 1941-By 1965

Description:	U.K. £	U.S. $	Can. $
Gloss	110.00	175.00	250.00

Model No. 927
CARDINAL

Designer: Arthur Gredington
Height: 5 3/4", 14.6 cm
Colours: Dark red - gloss
Issued: 1941-By 1959

Description:	U.K. £	U.S. $	Can. $
Gloss	95.00	150.00	200.00

Model No. 928
TANAGER

Designer:	Arthur Gredington
Height:	5 3/4", 14.6 cm
Colours:	1: Red - gloss
	2: Yellow, green and orange - gloss
	2: Various - gloss
Issued:	1941-1959

Description:	U.K. £	U.S. $	Can. $
1: Red	85.00	130.00	190.00
2: Yellow/green	85.00	130.00	190.00
3: Various	85.00	130.00	190.00

Model No. 929
CHICKADEE

Designer:	Arthur Gredington
Height:	5 3/4", 14.6 cm
Colours:	Dark and light blue, white and
	yellow - gloss or lustre
Issued:	1941-1968

Description:	U.K. £	U.S. $	Can. $
1: Gloss	75.00	120.00	160.00
2: Lustre	75.00	120.00	160.00

Model No. 930
PARAKEET

Designer:	Arthur Gredington
Height:	6", 15.0 cm
Colours:	Green and yellow - gloss
Issued:	1941-1975

Description:	U.K. £	U.S. $	Can. $
Gloss	75.00	120.00	160.00

Model No. 980A
ROBIN
First version - Base is green mound

Designer:	Arthur Gredington
Height:	3", 7.6 cm
Colours:	Brown and red - gloss
Issued:	1942-1973

Description:	U.K. £	U.S. $	Can. $
Gloss	35.00	55.00	75.00

Model No. 980B
ROBIN
Second version - Base is a branch and leaf

Designer:	Arthur Gredington
Re-modelled:	Albert Hallam
Height:	3", 7.6 cm
Colours:	Brown and red - gloss or matt
Issued:	1: Gloss - 1973 to the present
	2: Matt - 1983-1992

Description:	*U.K. £*	*U.S. $*	*Can. $*
1: Gloss	9.95	N/A	N/A
2: Matt	15.00	25.00	40.00

Model No. 991A
CHAFFINCH
First Version - Base is a green mound

Designer:	Arthur Gredington
Height:	2 3/4", 7.0 cm
Colours:	Pink, brown and black - gloss
Issued:	1943-1973

Description:	*U.K. £*	*U.S. $*	*Can. $*
Gloss	35.00	55.00	75.00

Model No. 991B
CHAFFINCH
Second Version - Base is a branch

Designer:	Arthur Gredington
Re-modelled:	Albert Hallam
Height:	2 3/4", 7.0 cm
Colours:	Pink, brown, black - gloss or matt
Issued:	1: Gloss - 1973 to the present
	2: Matt - 1983-1992

Description:	*U.K. £*	*U.S. $*	*Can. $*
1: Gloss	9.95	N/A	N/A
2: Matt	15.00	25.00	40.00

Model No. 992A
BLUE TIT
First Version - Base is a green mound

Designer:	Arthur Gredington
Height:	2 1/2", 6.4 cm
Colours:	White, blue and green - gloss
Issued:	1943-1973

Description:	*U.K. £*	*U.S. $*	*Can. $*
Gloss	35.00	55.00	75.00

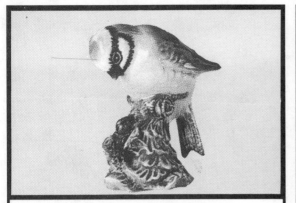

Model No. 992B
BLUETIT
Second Version - Base is branch and leaves

Designer:	Arthur Gredington
Remodelled:	Unknown
Height:	2 1/4", 5.7 cm
Colours:	White, blue and green - gloss or matt
Issued:	1: Gloss - 1973 to the present
	2: Matt - 1983-1992

Description:	U.K. £	U.S. $	Can. $
1: Gloss	9.95	N/A	N/A
2: Matt	15.00	25.00	40.00

Model No. 993A
WREN
First Version - Base is a green mound

Designer:	Arthur Gredington
Height:	2 1/4", 5.7 cm
Colours:	Light brown, pink breast - gloss
Issued:	1943-1973

Description:	U.K. £	U.S. $	Can. $
Gloss	35.00	55.00	75.00

Model No. 993B
WREN
Second Version - Base is a green leaf

Designer:	Arthur Gredington
Remodelled:	Graham Tongue
Height:	2 1/4", 5.7 cm
Colours:	Dark and light brown - gloss or matt
Issued:	1: Gloss - 1973 to the present
	2: Matt - 1983-1992

Description:	U.K. £	U.S. $	Can. $
1: Gloss	9.95	N/A	N/A
2: Matt	15.00	25.00	40.00

Model No. 994
SHELLDRAKE - Beak closed

Designer:	Arthur Gredington
Height:	6", 15.0 cm
Colours:	White, brown and green - gloss
Issued:	1943-1965

Description:	U.K. £	U.S. $	Can. $
Gloss	120.00	190.00	275.00

Model No. 995
SHELLDRAKE - Beak open

Designer:	Arthur Gredington
Height:	6 1/4", 15.9 cm
Colours:	White, brown and green - gloss
Issued:	1943-1965

Description:	*U.K. £*	*U.S. $*	*Can. $*
Gloss	120.00	195.00	275.00

Model No. 1001
COCKEREL

Designer:	Arthur Gredington
Height:	5 3/4", 14.6 cm
Colours:	Green, red and yellow - gloss
Issued:	1944-By 1959
Series:	Stylistic Models

Description:	*U.K. £*	*U.S. $*	*Can. $*
Gloss	125.00	200.00	275.00

Model No. 1004
ROOSTER

Designer:	Arthur Gredington
Height:	7", 17.8 cm
Colours:	White, green, red, blue and black - gloss
Issued:	1944-By 1959
Series:	Stylistic Model

Description:	*U.K. £*	*U.S. $*	*Can. $*
Gloss	125.00	200.00	275.00

Model No. 1006
GREBIE

Designer:	Arthur Gredington
Height:	5 1/4", 13.3 cm
Colours:	Green and browns - gloss
Issued:	1945-By 1954
Series:	Stylistic Model

Description:	*U.K. £*	*U.S. $*	*Can. $*
Gloss	175.00	275.00	375.00

Model No. 1009
COCK AND HEN - Salt and Pepper

Designer:	Unknown
Height:	2", 5.0 cm
Colours:	Teal green, brown, yellow and red - gloss
Issued:	1947-1959

Description:	U.K. £	U.S. $	Can. $
Gloss	45.00	70.00	100.00

Model No 1015
COURTING PENGUINS

Designer:	Arthur Gredington
Height:	5 1/2", 14.0 cm
Colours:	1: Black and white with yellow markings - gloss
	2: Blue - gloss
Is2sued:	1945-1965

Description:	U.K. £	U.S. $	Can. $
1: Black/white	120.00	190.00	275.00
2: Blue	120.00	190.00	275.00

Model No. 1018
BALD EAGLE

Designer:	Arthur Gredington
Height:	7 1/4", 18.4 cm
Colours:	Brown and white, blue and mauve base - gloss or matt
Issued:	1: Gloss - 1945-1995
	2: Matt - 1983-1989

Description:	U.K. £	U.S. $	Can. $
1: Gloss	55.00	95.00	135.00
2: Matt	55.00	95.00	135.00

Model No. 1022
TURTLE DOVES

Designer:	Arthur Gredington
Height:	7 1/2", 19.1 cm
Colours:	Browns, pale blue and pink, light brown and green base - gloss
Issued:	1945-1970

Description:	U.K. £	U.S. $	Can. $
Gloss	150.00	240.00	335.00

Model No. 1041A
GREY WAGTAIL
First Version - Head down, light green base

Designer: Arthur Gredington
Height: 2 1/2", 6.4 cm
Colours: Yellow, grey and black - gloss
Issued: Gloss - 1945-1973

Description:	U.K. £	U.S. $	Can. $
Gloss	35.00	55.00	75.00

Model No. 1041B
GREY WAGTAIL
Second Version - Head up, dark blue and green base

Designer: Arthur Gredington
Re-modelled: Albert Hallam
Height: 2 1/2", 6.4 cm
Colours: Yellow, grey and black - gloss or matt
Issued: 1: Gloss - 1973 to the present
              2: Matt - 1983-1989

Description:	U.K. £	U.S. $	Can. $
1: Gloss	9.95	N/A	N/A
2: Matt	15.00	25.00	40.00

Model No. 1042A
BULLFINCH
First Version - Yellow base and flowers

Designer: Arthur Gredington
Height: 2 1/2", 6.4 cm
Colours: Red breast, dark brown feathers,
              yellow flowers and base - gloss
Issued: 1945-1973

Description:	U.K. £	U.S. $	Can. $
Gloss	35.00	55.00	75.00

Model No. 1042B
BULLFINCH
Second Version - Base is a twig

Designer: Arthur Gredington
Re-modelled: Graham Tongue
Height: 2 1/2", 6.4 cm
Colours: Red, dark brown - gloss or matt
Issued: 1: Gloss - 1973 to the present
              2: Matt - 1983-1989

Description:	U.K. £	U.S. $	Can. $
1: Gloss	9.95	N/A	N/A
2: Matt	15.00	25.00	40.00

Model No. 1046A
BARN OWL
First Version - Split tail feathers

Designer:	Arthur Gredington
Height:	7 1/4", 18.4 cm
Colours:	Golden brown and white - gloss
Issued:	1946-Unknown

Description:	U.K. £	U.S. $	Can. $
Gloss	150.00	240.00	335.00

Model No. 1046B
BARN OWL
Second Version - Closed tail feathers

Designer:	Arthur Gredington
Height:	7 1/4", 18.4 cm
Colours:	Golden brown and white - gloss or matt
Issued:	1: Gloss - Unknown to the present
	2: Matt - 1983-1989

Description:	U.K. £	U.S. $	Can. $
1: Gloss	29.95	N/A	N/A
2: Matt	45.00	70.00	100.00

Model No. 1052
BARNACLE GOOSE

Designer:	Arthur Gredington
Height:	6 1/2", 16.5 cm
Colours:	Dark grey-blue and white - gloss
Issued:	1943-1968

Description:	U.K. £	U.S. $	Can. $
Gloss	325.00	500.00	700.00

Model No. 1159
KOOKABURRA

Designer:	Arthur Gredington
Height:	5 3/4", 14.6 cm
Colours:	Brown, blue and fawn - gloss
Issued:	1949-1976

Description:	U.K. £	U.S. $	Can. $
Gloss	120.00	190.00	275.00

Model No. 1178
GOULDIAN FINCH - Wings out

Designer:	Arthur Gredington
Height:	4", 10.1 cm
Colours:	Purple, green and yellow - gloss
Issued:	1949-By 1959

Description:	U.K. £	U.S. $	Can. $
Gloss	150.00	240.00	335.00

Model No. 1179
GOULDIAN FINCH - Wings in

Designer:	Arthur Gredington
Height:	4 1/2"", 11.9 cm
Colours:	Purple, green and yellow - gloss
Issued:	1949-By 1959

Description:	U.K. £	U.S. $	Can. $
Gloss	110.00	175.00	245.00

Model No. 1180
COCKATOO - Small

Designer:	Arthur Gredington
Height:	8 1/2", 21.6 cm
Colours:	1: Pink and grey - gloss
	2: Turquoise and yellow - gloss
Issued:	1949-1975

Description:	U.K. £	U.S. $	Can. $
1: Pink/grey	125.00	200.00	275.00
2: Turq./yellow	130.00	200.00	275.00

Note: Large version is model no. 1818.

Model No. 1212
DUCKS (Three) - Pintray

Designer:	Arthur Gredington
Height:	2 3/4", 7.0 cm
Colours:	1: Teal green, white and brown - gloss
	2: Blue - gloss
Issued:	1951-1971

Description:	U.K. £	U.S. $	Can. $
1: Teal green	35.00	55.00	75.00
2: Blue	35.00	55.00	75.00

Model No. 1216A
BUDGERIGAR - Facing left
First Version - Flowers in high relief on base

Designer: Arthur Gredington
Height: 7", 17.8 cm
Colours: 1: Blue and dark brown - gloss
             2: Green and yellow - gloss
Issued: 1951-1967

Description:	U.K. £	U.S. $	Can. $
1: Blue	150.00	240.00	335.00
2: Green	150.00	240.00	335.00

Model No. 1216B
BUDGERIGAR - Facing left
Second Version - No flowers on base

Designer: Arthur Gredington
Height: 7", 17.8 cm
Colours: Blue, green or yellow - gloss
Issued: 1: Blue - 1967-1975
             2: Green - 1967-1975
             3: Yellow - 1970-1972

Description:	U.K. £	U.S. $	Can. $
1: Blue	120.00	190.00	270.00
2: Green	120.00	190.00	270.00
3: Yellow	120.00	190.00	270.00

Model No. 1217A
BUDGERIGAR - Facing right
First Version - Flowers in high relief on base

Designer: Arthur Gredington
Height: 7", 17.8 cm
Colours: Blue or green - gloss
Issued: 1951-1967

Description:	U.K. £	U.S. $	Can. $
1: Blue	150.00	240.00	335.00
2: Green	150.00	240.00	335.00

Model No. 1217B
BUDGERIGAR - Facing right
Second Version - No flowers on base

Designer: Arthur Gredington
Height: 7", 17.8 cm
Colours: Blue or green - gloss
Issued: 1967-1970

Description:	U.K. £	U.S. $	Can. $
1: Blue	130.00	190.00	270.00
2: Green	130.00	190.00	270.00

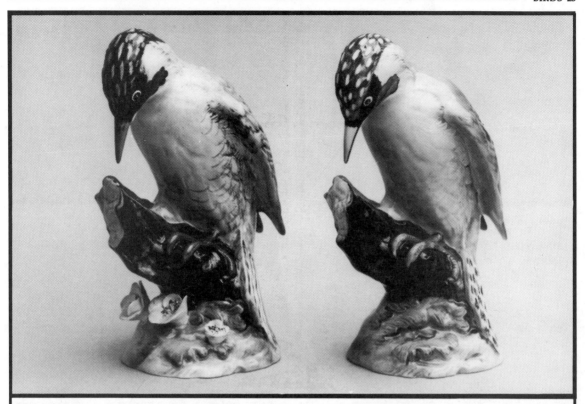

Model No. 1218A
GREEN WOODPECKER
First Version - Flowers in high relief on base

Designer:	Arthur Gredington
Height:	9", 22.9 cm
Colours:	Green, red and white - gloss
Issued:	1951-1967

Description:	U.K. £	U.S. $	Can. $
Gloss	175.00	275.00	395.00

Model No. 1218B
GREEN WOODPECKER
Second Version - No flowers on base

Designer:	Arthur Gredington
Height;	9", 22.9 cm
Colours:	Green, red and white - gloss or matt
Issued:	1: Gloss - 1967-1989
	2: Matt - 1983-1988

Description:	U.K. £	U.S. $	Can. $
1: Gloss	145.00	230.00	325.00
2: Matt	145.00	230.00	325.00

Model No. 1219A
JAY
First Version - Flowers in high relief on base

Designer:	Arthur Gredington		
Height:	6", 15.0 cm		
Colours:	Pink , blue and white - gloss		
Issued:	1951-1967		

Description:	*U.K. £*	*U.S. $*	*Can. $*
Gloss	135.00	215.00	300.00

Model No. 1219B
JAY
Second Version - No flowers on base

Designer:	Arthur Gredington		
Height:	6", 15.0 cm		
Colours:	Pink, blue and white - gloss		
Issued:	1967-1971		

Description:	*U.K. £*	*U.S. $*	*Can. $*
Gloss	120.00	190.00	270.00

Model No. 1225A
PHEASANT
First Version - Flowers in high relief on base

Designer:	Arthur Gredington		
Height:	7 3/4", 19.7 cm		
Colours:	Red-brown, teal green, green base - gloss		
Issued:	1951-1967		

Description:	*U.K. £*	*U.S. $*	*Can. $*
Gloss	145.00	230.00	235.00

Model No. 1225B
PHEASANT
Second Version - No flowers on base

Designer:	Arthur Gredington		
Height:	7 3/4", 19.7 cm		
Colours:	Red-brown, teal green, green base - gloss		
Issued:	1967-1977		

Description:	*U.K. £*	*U.S. $*	*Can. $*
Gloss	125.00	200.00	275.00

Model No. 1226A
PHEASANT
First Version - Flowers in high relief on base

Designer:	Arthur Gredington		
Height:	6", 15.0 cm		
Colours:	Red-brown, teal green, green base - gloss		
Issued:	1951-1967		

Description:	*U.K. £*	*U.S. $*	*Can. $*
Gloss	145.00	230.00	325.00

Model No. 1226B
PHEASANT
Second Version - No flowers on base

Designer:	Arthur Gredington		
Height:	6", 15.0 cm		
Colours:	Red-brown, teal green, green base - gloss		
Issued:	1967-1977		

Description:	*U.K. £*	*U.S. $*	*Can. $*
Gloss	125.00	200.00	275.00

Model No. 1383
PIGEON

Designer:	Mr. Orwell		
Height:	5 1/2", 14.0 cm		
Colours:	1: Blue or red - gloss or matt		
Issued:	1: Gloss - 1955-1989		
	2: Matt - 1983-1988		

Description:	*U.K. £*	*U.S. $*	*Can. $*
1A: Blue - gloss	95.00	150.00	215.00
1B: Blue - matt	95.00	150.00	215.00
2A: Red - gloss	95.00	150.00	215.00
2A: Red - matt	95.00	150.00	215.00

Model No. 1518

MALLARD DUCK

Designer: Arthur Gredington
Length: See below
Colours: Teal green, brown, white, yellow beak - gloss
Series: Peter Scott Wildfowl
Issued   See below

| | | | | Price | |
Description	Issued	Length	U.K. £	U.S. $	Can. $
Large	1958-1971	6 1/2", 16.5 cm	95.00	150.00	225.00
Medium	1859-1971	5 1/2", 14.0 cm	85.00	135.00	185.00
Small - First Version	1958-1962	4 1/2", 11.9 cm	75.00	120.00	175.00
Small - Second Version	1962-1971	3 3/4", 11.9 cm	75.00	120.00	165.00

Model No. 1519

MANDARIN DUCK

Designer: Arthur Gredington
Length: See below
Colours: Tan-brown and blue with red beak - gloss
Issued: 1958-1971
Series: Peter Scott Wildfowl

Description	Length	U.K. £	Price U.S. $	Can. $
Large	4 1/2", 11.9 cm	95.00	150.00	225.00
Medium	3 3/4", 9.5 cm	85.00	135.00	185.00
Small	3", 7.6 cm	75.00	120.00	165.00

Model No. 1520

POCHARD DUCK

Designer:	Arthur Gredington
Length:	See below
Colours:	Brown, grey and black - gloss
Issued:	1958-1971
Series:	Peter Scott Wildfowl

Description	Length	U.K. £	Price U.S. $	Can. $
Large	5 1/2", 14.0 cm	85.00	135.00	200.00
Medium	4 1/2", 11.9 cm	75.00	125.00	150.00
Small	3 1/2", 8.9 cm	85.00	135.00	200.00

Model No. 1521
KING EIDER DUCK

Designer:	Colin Melbourne
Length:	4", 10.1 cm
Colours:	Dark grey with tan, brown, green and white - gloss
Issued:	1958-1971
Series:	Peter Scott Wildfowl

Description:	U.K. £	U.S. $	Can. $
Gloss	85.00	135.00	190.00

Model No. 1522
SMEW DUCK

Designer:	Colin Melbourne
Length:	3", 7.6 cm
Colours:	Grey, black and white - gloss
Issued:	1958-1971
Series:	Peter Scott Wildfowl

Description:	U.K. £	U.S. $	Can. $
Gloss	85.00	135.00	190.00

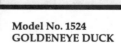

Model No. 1523
TUFTED DUCK

Designer:	Colin Melbourne
Length:	2 3/4", 7.0 cm
Colours:	Black and white - gloss
Issued:	1958-1971
Series:	Peter Scott Wildfowl

Description:	U.K. £	U.S. $	Can. $
Gloss	75.00	125.00	165.00

Model No. 1524
GOLDENEYE DUCK

Designer:	Colin Melbourne
Length:	3 1/2", 8.9 cm
Colours:	Black, white and green - gloss
Issued:	1958-1971
Series:	Peter Scott Wildfowl

Description:	U.K. £	U.S. $	Can. $
Gloss	85.00	135.00	190.00

Model No. 1525
GOOSANDER

Designer:	Colin Melbourne		
Length:	4 1/2", 11.9 cm		
Colours:	Pink, black and white, orange beak - gloss		
Issued:	1958-1971		
Series:	Peter Scott Wildfowl		

Description:	*U.K. £*	*U.S. $*	*Can. $*
Gloss	85.00	135.00	190.00

Model No. 1526
WIDGEON DUCK

Designer:	Colin Melbourne		
Length:	3 1/2", 8.9 cm		
Colours:	Pink, brown yellow, black and white - gloss		
Issued:	1958-1971		
Series:	Peter Scott Wildfowl		

Description:	*U.K. £*	*U.S. $*	*Can. $*
Gloss	75.00	125.00	165.00

Model No. 1527
SHELDUCK

Designer:	Colin Melbourne		
Length:	4", 10.1 cm		
Colours:	Dark grey, tan. white green and brown - gloss		
Issued:	1958-1971		
Series:	Peter Scott Wildfowl		

Description:	*U.K. £*	*U.S. $*	*Can. $*
Gloss	75.00	125.00	165.00

Model No. 1528
SHOVELER

Designer:	Colin Melbourne		
Length:	3 1/2", 8.9 cm		
Colours:	Tan, blue, white and dark brown - gloss		
Issued:	1958-1971		
Series:	Peter Scott Wildfowl		

Description:	*U.K. £*	*U.S. $*	*Can. $*
Gloss	75.00	125.00	165.00

Model No. 1529
TEAL DUCK

Designer:	Colin Melbourne
Length:	2 3/4", 7.0 cm
Colours:	Tan, yellow, black, white with blue beak - gloss
Issued:	1958-1971
Series:	Peter Scott Wildfowl

Description:	U.K. £	U.S. $	Can. $
Gloss	65.00	100.00	150.00

Model No. 1614
FANTAIL PIGEON

Designer:	Arthur Gredington
Height:	5", 12.7 cm
Colours:	White - gloss
Issued:	1959-1969

Description:	U.K. £	U.S. $	Can. $
Gloss	175.00	275.00	375.00

Model No. 1684
SWAN - Head up

Designer:	Arthur Gredington
Height:	3", 7.6 cm
Colours:	White - gloss
Issued:	1960-1973
Set:	1685, 1686, 1687

Description:	U.K. £	U.S. $	Can. $
Gloss	45.00	70.00	95.00

Model No. 1685
SWAN - Head down

Designer:	Arthur Gredington
Height:	2", 5.0 cm
Colours:	White - gloss
Issued:	1960-1973
Set:	1684, 1686, 1687

Description:	U.K £	U.S. $	Can. $
Gloss	45.00	70.00	95.00

Model No. 1686
CYGNET - Facing left

Designer:	Arthur Gredington
Height:	1", 2.5 cm
Colours:	Grey - gloss
Issued:	1960-1971
Set:	1684, 1685, 1687

Description:	U.K. £	U.S. $	Can. $
Gloss	45.00	70.00	95.00

Model No. 1687
CYGNET - Facing right

Designer:	Arthur Gredington
Height:	1", 2.5 cm
Colours:	Grey - gloss
Issued:	1960-1971
Set:	1684, 1685, 1686

Description:	U.K. £	U.S. $	Can. $
Gloss	45.00	70.00	95.00

Model No. 1774
PHEASANT - On pottery base

Designer:	Albert Hallam
Height:	4 3/4", 12.1 cm
Colours:	Red-brown, teal green and beige - gloss
Issued:	1961-1975

Description:	U.K. £	U.S. $	Can. $
Gloss	95.00	155.00	225.00

Model No. 1818
COCKATOO - Large

Designer:	Albert Hallam
Height:	11 1/2", 29.2 cm
Colours:	1: Pink and grey - gloss
	2: Turquoise and yellow - gloss
Issued:	1962-1973

Description:	U.K. £	U.S. $	Can. $
1: Pink/grey	165.00	250.00	350.00
2: Turq./yellow	165.00	250.00	350.00

Model No. 1892
LEGHORN COCKEREL

Designer:	Arthur Gredington
Height:	9", 22.9 cm
Colours:	Teal green, red, orange and yellow - gloss
Issued:	1963-1983

Description:	U.K. £	U.S. $	Can. $
Gloss	175.00	275.00	375.00

Model No. 1899
SUSSEX COCKEREL

Designer:	Arthur Gredington
Height:	7", 17.8 cm
Colours:	Black, white and pink - gloss
Issued:	1963-1971

Description:	U.K. £	U.S. $	Can. $
Gloss	225.00	350.00	500.00

Model No. 1957
TURKEY

Designer:	Albert Hallam
Height:	7 1/4", 18.4 cm
Colours:	1: Bronze - gloss
	2: White - gloss
Issued:	1964-1969

Description:	U.K. £	U.S. $	Can. $
1: Bronze	150.00	250.00	350.00
2: White	225.00	350.00	500.00

Model No. 2026
OWL

Designer:	Albert Hallam
Height:	4 1/2", 11.9 cm
Colours:	Golden brown and white - gloss
Issued:	1965 to the present

Description:	U.K. £	U.S. $	Can. $
Gloss	14.50	N/A	N/A

Model No. 2059
GAMECOCK

Designer: Arthur Gredington
Height: 9 1/2", 24.0 cm
Colours: Brown, teal green, cream and red - gloss
Issued: 1966-1975

Description:	U.K. £	U.S. $	Can. $
Gloss	225.00	350.00	500.00

Model No. 2062
GOLDEN EAGLE

Designer: Graham Tongue
Height: 9 1/2", 24.0 cm
Colours: Dark brown - gloss, matt, or satin matt
 Issued: 1: 1966-1974
             2: 1970-1972
             3: 1973-1989
Series: 3: Connoisseur

Description:	U.K. £	U.S. $	Can. $
1: Gloss	125.00	200.00	275.00
2: Matt	125.00	200.00	275.00
3: Satin matt	125.00	200.00	275.00

Model No. 2063
GROUSE (PAIR)

Designer: Albert Hallam
Height: 5 1/2", 14.0 cm
Colours: Red-brown - gloss
Issued: 1966-1975

Description:	U.K. £	U.S. $	Can. $
Gloss	175.00	275.00	350.00

Model No. 2064
PARTRIDGE (PAIR)

Designer: Albert Hallam
Height: 5 1/2", 14.0 cm
Colours: Brown and blue - gloss
Issued: 1966-1975

Description:	U.K. £	U.S. $	Can. $
Gloss	175.00	275.00	350.00

Photograph not
available at press time

Model No. 2067
TURKEY

Designer:	Albert Hallam
Height:	2 1/2", 6.4 cm
Colours:	1: White and red - gloss
	2: Bronze - gloss
Issued:	1966-1969

Description:	U.K. £	U.S. $	Can. $
1: White	75.00	110.00	150.00
2: Bronze	75.00	110.00	150.00

Model No. 2071
OWL

Designer:	Graham Tongue
Height:	5", 12.7 cm
Colours:	Unknown
Issued:	1966-Unknown
Series:	Contemporary Models

Description:	U.K. £	U.S. $	Can. $
Possibly not put into production.			

Model No. 2078
PHEASANTS (PAIR)

Designer:	Arthur Gredington
Height:	6 3/4", 17.2 cm
Colours:	Red-brown and teal green with
	yellow markings - gloss
Issued:	1966-1975

Description:	U.K. £	U.S. $	Can. $
Gloss	175.00	275.00	375.00

Model No. 2105A
GREENFINCH
First Version

Designer:	Graham Tongue
Height:	3", 7.6 cm
Colours:	Green and yellow - gloss
Issued:	Gloss: 1967-1973

Description:	U.K. £	U.S. $	Can. $
Gloss	35.00	55.00	75.00

Photograph not
available at press time

Model No. 2105B
GREENFINCH
Second Version

Designer: Graham Tongue
Re-modelled: Albert Hallam
Height: 3", 7.6 cm
Colours: Natural - gloss or matt
Issued: 1: Gloss - 1973 to the present
               2: Matt - 1983-1992

Description:	U.K. £	U.S. $	Can. $
1: Gloss	9.95	N/A	N/A
2: Matt	15.00	25.00	35.00

Model No. 2106A
WHITETHROAT
First Version - Mouth open, base is a green mound

Designer: Graham Tongue
Height: 3", 7.6 cm
Colours: Dark grey, white and pink - gloss
Issued: 1967-1973

Description:	U.K. £	U.S. $	Can. $
Gloss	35.00	55.00	75.00

Model No. 2106B
WHITETHROAT
Second Version - Mouth closed, base is a leaf

Designer: Graham Tongue
Remodelled: Albert Hallam
Height: 3", 7.6 cm
Colours: Natural - gloss or matt
Issued: 1: Gloss - 1973 to the presemt
             2: Matt - 1983-1992

Description:	U.K. £	U.S. $	Can. $
1: Gloss	11.50	N/A	N/A
2: Matt	15.00	25.00	35.00

Model No. 2183
BALTIMORE ORIOLE

Designer: Albert Hallam
Height: 3 1/2", 8.9 cm
Colours: Black and red - gloss or matt
Issued: 1: Gloss - 1968-1973
            2: Matt - 1970-1972

Description:	U.K. £	U.S. $	Can. $
1: Gloss	95.00	150.00	200.00
2: Matt	95.00	150.00	200.00

Model No. 2184
CEDAR WAXWING

Designer: Graham Tongue
Height: 4 1/2", 11.9 cm
Colours: Brown, black and yellow - gloss or matt
Issued: 1: Gloss - 1968-1973
2: Matt - 1970-1972

Description:	U.K. £	U.S. $	Can. $
1: Gloss	95.00	150.00	200.00
2: Matt	95.00	150.00	200.00

Model No. 2187
AMERICAN ROBIN

Designer: Graham Tongue
Height: 4", 10.1 cm
Colours: Dark grey and red - gloss or matt
Issued: 1: Gloss - 1968-1973
2: Matt - 1970-1972

Description:	U.K. £	U.S. $	Can. $
1: Gloss	95.00	150.00	200.00
2: Matt	95.00	150.00	200.00

Model No. 2188
BLUE JAY

Designer: Albert Hallam
Height: 4 1/2", 11.9 cm
Colours: Blue and white - gloss or matt
Issued: 1: Gloss - 1968-1973
2: Matt - 1970 - 1972

Description:	U.K. £	U.S. $	Can. $
1: Gloss	95.00	150.00	200.00
2: Matt	95.00	150.00	200.00

Model No. 2189
BLACK CAPPED CHICADEE

Designer: Graham Tongue
Height: 4 1/2", 11.9 cm
Colours: Yellow, white, grey, green
and black - gloss or matt
Issued: 1: Gloss - 1968-1973
2: Matt - 1970-1972

Description:	U.K. £	U.S. $	Can. $
1: Gloss	95.00	150.00	200.00
2: Matt	95.00	150.00	200.00

Model No. 2190
EVENING GROSBEAK

Designer: Albert Hallam
Height: 4", 10.1 cm
Colours: Black and yellow - gloss or matt
Issued: 1: Gloss - 1968-1973
2: Matt - 1970-1972

Description:	U.K. £	U.S. $	Can. $
1: Gloss	95.00	150.00	200.00
2: Matt	110.00	175.00	250.00

Model No. 2191
QUAIL

Designer: Albert Hallam
Height: 5", 12.7 cm
Colours: Browns, black and white - gloss or matt
Issued: 1: Gloss - 1968-1971
2: Matt - 1970-1972

Description:	U.K. £	U.S. $	Can. $
1: Gloss	110.00	175.00	250.00
2: Matt	110.00	175.00	250.00

Model No. 2200
CHICKEN - Running

Designer: Graham Tongue
Height: 1 1/4", 3.2 cm
Colours: Yellow - gloss
Issued: 1968-1973
Set: 2201, 2202

Description:	U.K. £	U.S. $	Can. $
Gloss	75.00	120.00	150.00

Model No. 2201
CHICKEN - Pecking

Designer: Graham Tongue
Height: 1", 2.5 cm
Colours: Yellow - gloss
Issued: 1968-1973
Set: 2200, 2202

Description:	U.K. £	U.S. $	Can. $
Gloss	75.00	120.00	150.00

Model No. 2202
CHICKEN - Sitting

Designer:	Graham Tongue		
Height:	1 1/2", 3.8cm		
Colours:	Yellow - gloss		
Issued:	1968-1973		
Set:	2200, 2201		

Description:	U.K. £	U.S. $	Can. $
Gloss	75.00	120.00	150.00

Photograph not
available at press time

Model No. 2238
OWL

Designer:	Harry Sales		
Height:	6 3/4", 17.2 cm		
Colours:	Unknown		
Issued:	1968-1971		
Series:	Moda Range		

Description:	U.K. £	U.S. $	Can. $
	175.00	275.00	395.00

Photograph not
available at press time

Model No. 2239
BIRD

Designer:	Harry Sales		
Height:	5", 12.7 cm		
Colours:	Unknown		
Issued:	1968-1971		
Series:	Moda Range		

Description:	U.K. £	U.S. $	Can. $
	175.00	275.00	395.00

Model No. 2240
COCKEREL

Designer:	Harry Sales		
Height:	6", 15.0 cm		
Colours:	1: Blue - gloss		
	2: Brown - matt		
Issued:	1968-1971		
Series:	Moda Range		

Description:	U.K. £	U.S. $	Can. $
1: Blue	65.00	100.00	150.00
2: Brown	65.00	100.00	150.00

Model No. 2273
GOLDFINCH

Designer: Graham Tongue
Height: 3", 7.6 cm
Colours: Brown, white, red and yellow
           - gloss or matt
Issued: 1: Gloss - 1969 to the present
           2: Matt - 1983-1992

Description:	U.K. £	U.S. $	Can. $
1: Gloss	11.50	N/A	N/A
2: Matt	15.00	25.00	35.00

Model No. 2274
STONECHAT

Designer: Albert Hallam
Height: 3", 7.6 cm
Colours: Dark brown and white, red breast
           - gloss or matt
Issued: 1: Gloss - 1969 to the present
           2: Matt - 1983-1992

Description:	U.K. £	U.S. $	Can. $
1: Gloss	9.95	N/A	N/A
2: Matt	15.00	25.00	35.00

Model No. 2305
MAGPIE

Designer: Albert Hallam
Height: 5", 12.7 cm
Colours: Black and white - gloss
Issued: 1970-1982

Description:	U.K. £	U.S. $	Can. $
Gloss	110.00	175.00	225.00

Model No. 2307
EAGLE ON ROCK

Designer: Graham Tongue
Height: 3 3/4", 9.5 cm
Colours: Browns - gloss
Issued: 1970-1975

Description:	U.K. £	U.S. $	Can. $
Gloss	75.00	125.00	175.00

Model No. 2308
SONGTHRUSH

Designer:	Albert Hallam
Height:	5 3/4", 14.6 cm
Colours:	Brown with yellow speckled breast - gloss and matt
Issued:	1: Gloss - 1970-1989
	2: Matt - 1983-1989

Description:	U.K. £	U.S. $	Can. $
1: Gloss	110.00	175.00	225.00
2: Matt	110.00	175.00	225.00

Model No. 2315
CUCKOO

Designer:	Albert Hallam
Height:	5", 12.7 cm
Colours:	Blue - gloss
Issued:	1970-1982

Description:	U.K. £	U.S. $	Can. $
Gloss	110.00	175.00	225.00

Model No. 2316
KESTREL

Designer:	Graham Tongue
Height:	6 3/4", 17.2 cm
Colours:	Browns, white and blue - gloss or matt
Issued:	1: Gloss - 1970-1989
	2: Matt - 1983-1989

Description:	U.K. £	U.S. $	Can. $
1: Gloss	95.00	150.00	215.00
2: Matt	95.00	150.00	215.00

Model No. 2357
PENGUIN

Designer: Albert Hallam
Height: 12", 30.5 cm
Colours: Black and white - gloss
Issued: 1971-1976
Series: Fireside Model

Description:	*U.K. £*	*U.S. $*	*Can. $*
Gloss	300.00	475.00	675.00

Photograph not
available at press time

Model No. 2359
HERON - Stylistic

Designer: Albert Hallam
Height: 10 1/2", 26.7 cm
Colours: Unknown
Issued: 1971-Unknown

Description:	*U.K. £*	*U.S. $*	*Can. $*
		Extremely Rare	

Model No. 2371
KINGFISHER

Designer: Albert Hallam
Height: 5", 12.7 cm
Colours: Blue and brown - gloss or matt
Issued: 1: Gloss - 1971 to the present
              2: Matt - 1983-1989

Description:	*U.K. £*	*U.S. $*	*Can. $*
Gloss	29.95	N/A	N/A
Matt	45.00	70.00	100.00

Photograph not
available at press time

Model No. 2398
PENGUIN CHICK - Standing

Designer:	Graham Tongue
Height:	7", 17.8 cm
Colours:	Blue, black and white - gloss
Issued:	1971-1976

Description:	*U.K. £*	*U.S. $*	*Can. $*
Gloss	150.00	250.00	335.00

Model No. 2399
PENGUIN CHICK

Designer:	Albert Hallam
Height:	6 3/4", 17.2 cm
Colours:	Black and white - gloss
Issued:	1972-Unknown

Description:	*U.K. £*	*U.S. $*	*Can. $*
	Probably not put into production		

Modle No. 2413
NUTHATCH

Designer:	Graham Tongue
Height:	3", 7.6 cm
Colours:	Dark blue and white - gloss or matt
Issued:	1: Gloss - 1972 to the present
	2: Matt - 1983-1989

Description:	*U.K. £*	*U.S. $*	*Can. $*
1: Gloss	9.95	N/A	N/A
2: Matt	15.00	25.00	35.00

Model No. 2415
GOLDCREST

Designer:	Graham Tongue
Height:	3", 7.6 cm
Colours:	Green, yellow and grey - gloss or matt
Issued:	1: Gloss - 1972 to the present
	2: Matt - 1983-1989

Description:	*U.K. £*	*U.S. $*	*Can. $*
1: Gloss	9.95	N/A	N/A
2: Matt	15.00	25.00	35.00

Model No. 2416
LAPWING

Designer:	Albert Hallam
Height:	5 1/2", 14.0 cm
Colours:	Black, dark green and white - gloss
Issued:	1972-1982

Description:	U.K. £	U.S. $	Can. $
Gloss	95.00	150.00	215.00

Model No. 2417
JAY

Designer:	Graham Tongue
Height:	5", 12.7 cm
Colours:	Brown, white and blue - gloss
Issued:	1972-1982

Description:	U.K. £	U.S. $	Can. $
Gloss	95.00	150.00	215.00

Model No. 2420
LESSER SPOTTED WOODPECKER

Designer:	Graham Tongue
Height:	5 1/2", 14.0 cm
Colours:	Red, white and black - gloss
Issued:	1972-1982

Description:	U.K. £	U.S. $	Can. $
Gloss	95.00	150.00	215.00

Model No. 2434
PENGUIN CHICK - Sliding

Designer:	Graham Tongue
Height:	3 3/4" x 8", 9.5 x 20.3 cm
Colours:	Blue, black and white - gloss
Issued:	1972-1976

Description:	U.K. £	U.S. $	Can. $
Gloss	195.00	300.00	425.00

Model No. 2760
PHEASANT

Designer:	Graham Tongue
Height:	10 1/2", 26.7 cm
Colours:	Tan and brown - satin matt
Issued:	1982-1989
Series:	Connoisseur

Description:	U.K. £	U.S. $	Can. $
Satin matt	110.00	175.00	250.00

Note: Transferred to Royal Doulton backstamp
(DA 38 "Open Ground") 08/89.

Model No. 3272
TAWNY OWL

Designer:	Mr. Sutton
Height:	3 1/4", 8.3 cm
Colours:	Brown and white - gloss
Issued:	1990 to the present

Description:	U.K. £	U.S. $	Can. $
Gloss	9.95	N/A	N/A

Model No. 3273
BARN OWL

Designer:	Martyn C. R. Alcock
Height:	3 1/4", 8.3 cm
Colours:	Light brown and white - gloss
Issued:	1990 to the present

Description:	U.K. £	U.S. $	Can. $
Gloss	9.95	N/A	N/A

Model No. 3274
GREAT TIT

Designer: Martyn C R. Alcock
Height: 3", 7.6 cm
Colours: Black, yellow, white and grey - gloss
Issued: 1990 to the present

Description:	U.K. £	U.S. $	Can. $
Gloss	11.50	N/A	N/A

Model No. 3275
KINGFISHER

Designer: Mr. Sutton
Height: 2 3/4", 7.0 cm
Colours: Blue head and wings, orange breast - gloss
Issued: 1990 to the present

Description:	U.K. £	U.S. $	Can. $
Gloss	9.95	N/A	N/A

BIRD WALL PLAQUES

INDEX BY MODEL NUMBER

Model No. 596

MALLARD

Designer:	Mr. Watkin
Height:	See below
Issued:	See below
Colours:	1: Brown, teal green and white - gloss
	2: White with yellow beaks - matt

Model No. Finish		Issued	Height	U.K. £	U.S. $	Can. $
596/0	Gloss	1938-1971	11 3/4", 29.8 cm	65.00	90.00	145.00
596/0	Matt	1938-1971	11 3/4", 29.8 cm	65.00	90.00	145.00
596/1	Gloss	1938-1973	10", 25.4 cm	55.00	80.00	125.00
596/1	Matt	1938-1973	10", 25.4 cm	55.00	80.00	125.00
596/2	Gloss	1938-1973	8 3/4", 22.2 cm	45.00	70.00	100.00
596/2	Matt	1938-1973	8 3/4", 22.2 cm	45.00	70.00	100.00
596/3	Gloss	1938-1973	7", 17.8 cm	45.00	70.00	100.00
596/3	Matt	1938-1973	7", 17.8 cm	45.00	70.00	100.00
596/4	Gloss	1938-1971	5 3/4", 14.6 cm	35.00	55.00	75.00
596/4	Matt	1938-1971	5 3/4", 14.6 cm	35.00	55.00	75.00

Note: These also exist with a small "pocket" between the wings.

Model No. 658

SEAGULL
Style One - Wings up, apart

Designer:	Mr. Watkin
Height:	See below
Colours:	1: White, black and yellow - gloss
	2: White - matt
Issued:	1938-1967

Model No.	Finish	Length	U.K. £	Price U.S. $	Can. $
658/1	Gloss	14", 35.5 cm	65.00	100.00	145.00
658/1	Matt	14", 35.5 cm	65.00	100.00	145.00
658/2	Gloss	11 3/4", 29.8 cm	55.00	80.00	125.00
658/2	Matt	11 3/4", 29.8 cm	55.00	80.00	125.00
658/3	Gloss	10", 25.4 cm	45.00	70.00	100.00
658/3	Matt	10", 25.4 cm	45.00	70.00	100.00
658/4	Gloss	8", 20.3 cm	45.00	70.00	100.00
658/4	Matt	8", 20.3 cm	45.00	70.00	100.00

Model No. 661

PHEASANT

Designer: Mr. Watkin
Length: See below
Colours: 1: Teal green, browns and white - gloss
            2: White - matt
Issued: 1938-1971

Model No.	Finish	Length	U.K. £	Price U.S. $	Can. $
661/1	Gloss	12", 30.5 cm	65.00	90.00	100.00
661/1	Matt	12", 30.5 cm	65.00	90.00	100.00
661/2	Gloss	10 1/4", 26.0 cm	55.00	80.00	125.00
661/2	Matt	10 1/4", 26.0 cm	55.00	80.00	125.00
661/3	Gloss	8 1/2", 21.6 cm	45.00	70.00	100.00
661/3	Mat	8 1/2", 21.6 cm	45.00	70.00	100.00

Model No. 705
BLUE TIT - Flying to the right

Designer:	Mr. Watkin
Height:	4 1/2", 11.9 cm
Size:	Large
Colours:	Blue and browns - gloss
Issued:	1939-1967
Set:	706, 707

Description::	U.K. £	U.S. $	Can. $
Gloss	55.00	80.00	125.00

Model No. 706
BLUE TIT - Flying to the left

Designer:	Mr. Watkin
Height:	4 1/2", 11.9 cm
Size:	Medium
Colours:	Blue and browns - gloss
Issued:	1939-1967
Set:	705, 707

Description:	U.K. £	U.S. $	Can. $
Gloss	55.00	80.00	125.00

Model No. 707
BLUE TIT - Wings up, flying to the left

Designer:	Mr. Watkin
Height:	4 1/2", 11.9 cm
Size:	Small
Colours:	Blue and browns - gloss
Issued:	1939-1967
Set:	705, 706

Description:	U.K. £	U.S. $	Can. $
Gloss	55.00	80.00	125.00

Model No. 729

KINGFISHER

Designer: Arthur Gredington
Height: See below
Colours: Green and yellow - gloss
Issued: 1939-1971

Model No.	Finish	Length	U.K. £	Price U.S. $	Can. $
729/1	Gloss	7 1/2", 19.1 cm	65.00	90.00	145.00
729/1	Matt	7 1/2", 19.1 cm	65.00	90.00	145.00
729/2	Gloss	6", 15.0 cm	45.00	70.00	100.00
729/2	Matt	6", 15.0 cm	45.00	70.00	100.00
729/3	Gloss	5", 12.7 cm	45.00	70.00	100.00
729/3	Matt	5", 12.7 cm	45.00	70.00	100.00

Note: Model no. 729/2 can be paired with no. 743 to make a facing pair.

Photograph not
available at press time

Model No. 731
FLAMINGO

Designer:	Mr. Watkin
Length:	15", 38.1 cm
Colours:	Pearl orange and black - gloss
Issued:	1939-1954

Description:	U.K. £	U.S. $	Can. $
Gloss	200.00	325.00	450.00

Model No. 743
KINGFISHER

Designer:	Arthur Gredington
Height:	6", 15.0 cm
Colours:	Greens and yellow - gloss
Issued:	1939-1954

Description:	U.K. £	U.S. $	Can. $
Gloss	45.00	70.00	100.00

Note: Model no. 743 can be paired with no. 729/2 to make a facing pair.

Model No. 757

SWALLOW

Designer: Arthur Gredington
Height: See below
Colours: Blues - gloss
Issued: 1939-1973

Model No.	Size	Length	U.K. £	Price U.S. $	Can. $
757/1	Large	7 1/2", 19.1 cm	65.00	90.00	145.00
757/2	Medium	6 1/4", 15.9 cm	55.00	80.00	125.00
757/3	Small	5", 12.7 cm	45.00	70.00	100.00

Model No. 922
SEAGULL
Style Two - Wings up, together
Designer: Arthur Gredington
Height: Large - 12", 30.5 cm
              Medium - 10 1/2", 26.7 cm
              Small - 9 1/2", 24.0 cm
Colours: White, grey and black - gloss or matt
Issued: 1941-1971

Description:	U.K. £	U.S. $	Can. $
Large - gloss	75.00	125.00	165.00
Large - matt	75.00	125.00	165.00
Medium - gloss	65.00	90.00	145.00
Medium - matt	65.00	90.00	145.00
Small - gloss	55.00	80.00	125.00
Small - matt	55.00	80.00	125.00

Model No. 1023
HUMMING BIRD

Designer: Arthur Gredington
Height: Large - 5 3/4", 14.6 cm
              Medium - 5", 12.7 cm
              Small - 4 3/4", 12.1 cm
Colours: Browns, grey and red - gloss
Issued: 1944-1967

Description:	U.K. £	U.S. $	Can. $
Large - gloss	95.00	150.00	200.00
Large - matt	95.00	150.00	200.00
Medium - gloss	85.00	135.00	190.00
Medium - matt	85.00	135.00	190.00
Smal - gloss	75.00	125.00	165.00
Small - matt	75.00	125.00	165.00

Model No. 1188

PINK LEGGED PARTRIDGE

Designer: Arthur Gredington
Height: See below
Colours: Browns, white and grey - gloss
Issued: 1950-1967

Model No.	Size	Length	U.K. £	Price U.S. $	Can. $
1188/1	Large	10 1/2", 26.7 cm	95.00	150.00	200.00
1188/2	Medium	9", 22.9 cm	85.00	135.00	190.00
1188/3	Small	7 1/2", 19.1 cm	75.00	125.00	165.00

Model No. 1344

GREEN WOODPECKER

Designer: Mr. Orwell
Height: See below
Colours: Greens and brown, red head - gloss
Issued: 1954-1968

Model No.	Finish	Length	U.K. £	Price U.S. $	Can. $
1344/1	Large	7 1/2", 19.1 cm	95.00	150.00	200.00
1344/2	Medium	6", 15.0 cm	85.00	135.00	190.00
1344/3	Small	5", 12.7 cm	75.00	125.00	165.00

Model No. 1530

TEAL

Designer: Arthur Gredington
Height: See Below
Colours: Brown, grey and green - gloss
Issued: 1958-1968

Model No.	Size	Length	U.K. £	Price U.S. $	Can. $
1530/1	Large	8 1/4"", 21.0 cm	95.00	150.00	200.00
1530/2	Medium	7 1/4", 18.4 cm	85.00	135.00	190.00
1530/3	Small	6 1/4", 15.9 cm	75.00	125.00	165.00

Chapter Two
BUTTERFLY PLAQUES

Butterflies are an unusual choice for the medium of pottery, and these few wall plaques tend to be rare. It is also unusual to find them in perfect condition, as often the antennae have suffered from the passage of time. These butterfly wall plaques were modelled in large, medium and small sizes. The Beswick attention to detail is very apparent here.

At the present time, the information on these models is virtually nonexistent, and there have been no catalogues found in which they are illustrated. Fortunately, each model is impressed on the back with the name of the butterfly and the shape number. If this were not the case, then identification would be a problem.

INDEX BY MODEL NUMBER

Model No. 1487

PURPLE EMPEROR BUTTERFLY

Designer: Albert Hallam
Height: 6 1/4" x 4", 15.9 x 10.1 cm
Size: Large

Colours	Issued	U.K. £	Price U.S. $	Can. $
Blue and white - gloss	1957-By 1963	175.00	275.00	395.00

Model No. 1488
RED ADMIRAL BUTTERFLY

Designer: Albert Hallam
Dimensions: 6 1/4" x 4", 15.9 x 10.1 cm
Size: Large
Colours: Browns, blue and white - gloss
Issued: 1957-By 1963

Description:	U.K. £	U.S. $	Can. $
Gloss	175.00	275.00	395.00

Model No. 1489
PEACOCK BUTTERFLY

Designer: Albert Hallam
Dimensions: 6 1/4" x 4", 15.9 x 10.1 cm
Size: Large
Colours: Browns, black and yellow - gloss
Issued: 1957-By 1963

Description:	U.K. £	U.S. $	Can. $
Gloss	175.00	275.00	395.00

Model No. 1490
CLOUDED YELLOW BUTTERFLY

Designer: Albert Hallam
Dimensions: 5 1/4" x 3 1/2", 13.3 x 8.9 cm
Size: Medium
Colours: Yellow, black and red - gloss
Issued: 1957-By 1963

Description:	U.K. £	U.S. $	Can. $
Gloss	175.00	275.00	395.00

Model No. 1491
TORTOISESHELL BUTTERFLY

Designer: Albert Hallam
Dimensions: 5 1/4" x 3 1/2", 13.3 x 8.9 cm
Size: Medium
Colours: Yellow, blue and black - gloss
Issued: 1957-By 1963

Description:	U.K. £	U.S. $	Can. $
Gloss	175.00	275.00	395.00

Photograph not
available at press time

Model No. 1492
SWALLOW-TAIL BUTTERFLY

Designer: Albert Hallam
Dimensions: 5 1/4" x 3 1/2", 13.3 x 8.9 cm
Size: Medium
Colours: Unknown - gloss
Issued: 1957-By 1963

Description:	U.K. £	U.S. $	Can. $
Gloss	175.00	275.00	395.00

Photograph not
available at press time

Model No. 1493
SMALL COPPER BUTTERFLY

Designer: Albert Hallam
Dimensions: 3 3/4" x 2 1/4", 9.5 x 5.7 cm
Size: Small
Colours: Unknown - gloss
Issued: 1957-By 1963

Description:	U.K. £	U.S. $	Can. $
Gloss	150.00	240.00	330.00

Model No. 1494
PURPLE HAIRSTREAK BUTTERFLY

Designer: Albert Hallam
Dimensions: 3 3/4" x 2 1/4", 9.5 x 5.7 cm
Size: Small
Colours: Browns and grey - gloss
Issued: 1957-By 1963

Description:	U.K. £	U.S. $	Can. $
Gloss	150.00	240.00	330.00

Photograph not
available at press time

Model No. 1495
SMALL HEATH BUTTERFLY

Designer: Albert Hallam
Dimensions: 3 3/4" x 2 1/4", 9.5 x 5.7 cm
Size: Small
Colours: Unknown - gloss
Issued: 1957-By 1963

Description:	U.K. £	U.S. $	Can. $
Gloss	150.00	240.00	330.00

Chapter Three

CATS

Cat lovers will appreciate the variety of felines offered here. As well as realistic models, there are cats playing instruments and playing ball, zodiac cats and cats just clowning around.

These figures were also produced in a large selection of colours and finishes:

COLOUR	FINISH
Black	Gloss or matt; Satin matt
Black and white	Gloss
Chocolate point	Gloss
Copper lustre	Gloss
Ginger:	Gloss or matt
Ginger striped	Gloss
Ginger Swiss roll	Gloss
Grey	Gloss or matt
Grey striped	Gloss
Grey Swiss roll (tabby)	Gloss
Lead grey (British blue)	Gloss
Seal point	Gloss or matt
Royal blue	Gloss
White	Gloss or matt; Satin matt

The research on the production dates for the various colourways of the cats was not completed in time for this edition. Work is continuing on the data which will be ready for the second edition.

Collectors should note that all colourways were not issued for the total length of the model issue period. Some colourways had a very short life span. For example lead grey (British blue) was discontinued in most cases by 1966.

The second edition will also carry colour plates which will help to distinguish the confusing range of cat colours.

INDEX BY MODEL NUMBER

Model No. 1026
CAT CONDUCTOR

Designer:	Arthur Gredington
Height:	2", 5.0 cm
Colours:	Grey striped - gloss
Issued:	1945-1973
Series:	Cat Orchestra
Set:	1027, 1028, 1029

Description:	U.K. £	U.S. $	Can. $
Gloss	45.00	75.00	100.00

Model No. 1027
CAT WITH CELLO

Designer:	Arthur Gredington
Height:	2", 5.0 cm
Colours:	Grey striped - gloss
Issued:	1945-1973
Series:	Cat Orchestra
Set:	1026, 1028, 1029

Description:	U.K. £	U.S. $	Can. $
Gloss	45.00	75.00	100.00

Model No. 1028
CAT WITH FIDDLE

Designer:	Arthur Gredington
Height:	2", 5.0 cm
Colours:	Grey striped - gloss
Issued:	1945-1973
Series:	Cat Orchestra
Set:	1026, 1027, 1029

Description:	U.K. £	U.S. $	Can. $
Gloss	45.00	75.00	100.00

Model No. 1029
CAT WITH SAXOPHONE

Designer:	Arthur Gredington
Height:	2", 5.0 cm
Colours:	Grey striped - gloss
Issued:	1945-1973
Series:	Cat Orchestra
Set:	1026, 1027, 1028

Description:	U.K. £	U.S. $	Can. $
Gloss	45.00	75.00	100.00

Model No. 1030
CAT - Seated, head looks up

Designer: Arthur Gredington
Height: 6 1/4", 15.9 cm
Colours: See below - gloss
Issued: 1945-1973

Description:	U.K. £	U.S. $	Can. $
Ginger	65.00	100.00	150.00
Ginger Stripe	95.00	150.00	200.00
Grey	65.00	100.00	150.00
Dark grey	55.00	85.00	125.00
Royal blue	95.00	150.00	200.00
White - 1945-1964	60.00	95.00	135.00
White - 1964-1973	50.00	80.00	110.00

Note: There are two shades of white.
    1: 1945-1964 - soft, smaller eyes
    2: 1964-1973 - more theatrical eyes, heavy painting

Model No. 1031
CAT - Seated, head looks forward

Designer: Arthur Gredington
Height: 4 1/2", 11.9 cm
Colours: See below - gloss
Issued: 1945-1973

Description:	U.K. £	U.S. $	Can. $
Ginger	50.00	80.00	110.00
Ginger stripe	65.00	100.00	150.00
Grey	50.00	80.00	110.00
Dark grey	55.00	85.00	125.00
Grey stripe	50.00	80.00	110.00
White	50.00	80.00	110.00

Model No. 1296
SIAMESE KITTENS - Curled together

Designer: Miss Granoska   Length: 2 3/4", 7.0 cm

Colours	Issued	U.K. £	Price U.S. $	Can. $
Chocolate point - gloss	1953–c.1982	35.00	55.00	75.00
Seal point - gloss	c.1982-1989	35.00	55.00	75.00
Seal point - matt	1984-1989	55.00	85.00	125.00
Copper lustre - gloss	1971 (export only)	95.00	150.00	200.00
One white/one pale grey - gloss	Unknown	75.00	125.00	165.00

Note: Transferred to R.D. backstamp (DA122) 08/89, seal point - gloss.

Model No. 1316
PERSIAN KITTENS - Seated

Designer:	Miss Granoska
Height:	3 1/2", 8.9 cm
Colours:	See below - gloss
Issued:	1953-1973

Description:	U.K. £	U.S. $	Can. $
Ginger	35.00	55.00	75.00
Ginger stripe	50.00	85.00	110.00
Grey	35.00	55.00	75.00
Grey stripe	45.00	75.00	100.00
Dark grey	35.00	55.00	75.00
White	35.00	55.00	75.00

Model No. 1435
CAT - Seated

Designer:	Colin Melbourne
Height:	5 1/4", 13.3 cm
Colours:	Grey stripe - gloss
Issued:	1956-1963

Description:	U.K. £	U.S. $	Can. $
Gloss	110.00	175.00	250.00

Model No. 1436
KITTEN - Seated

Designer:	Colin Melbourne
Height:	3 1/4", 8.3 cm
Colours:	Ginger; Grey; Grey stripe; White - gloss
	Black; Ginger; Grey; White - matt
Issued:	Gloss: 1956-1989
	Matt: 1984-1989

Description:	U.K. £	U.S. $	Can. $
Black - gloss	25.00	40.00	50.00
Black - matt	30.00	45.00	65.00
Ginger - gloss	15.00	25.00	35.00
Ginger - matt	20.00	30.00	45.00
Ginger stripe - gloss	35.00	55.00	75.00
Grey - gloss	20.00	30.00	45.00
Grey - matt	25.00	40.00	50.00
Grey stripe - gloss	25.00	40.00	50.00
White - gloss	15.00	25.00	35.00
White - matt	25.00	40.00	50.00

Note: Transferred to the R.D. backstamp (DA123) 08/89 in ginger, grey, white - gloss.

Model No. 1437
CAT - Seated, looking up

Designer:	Colin Melbourne
Height:	3 1/4", 8.3 cm
Colours:	Grey stripe - gloss
Issued:	1956-1963

Description:	U.K. £	U.S. $	Can. $
Grey stripe	95.00	150.00	225.00

Model No. 1438
CAT - Standing, looking back

Designer:	Colin Melbourne
Height:	3 3/4", 9.5 cm
Colours:	Grey stripe - gloss
Issued:	1956-1963

Description:	U.K. £	U.S. $	Can. $
Grey stripe	95.00	150.00	225.00

Photograph not
available at press time

Photograph not
available at press time

Model No. 1541
CAT - Seated

Designer: Mr. Garbet
Height: Unknown
Colours: Unknown
Issued: 1958-1961

Description: *U.K. £*   *U.S. $*   *Can. $*
                        Extremely Rare

Model No. 1542
CAT - Lying, left front paw up

Designer: Mr. Garbet
Height: Unknown
Colours: Unknown
Issued: 1958-1961

Description: *U.K. £*   *U.S. $*   *Can. $*
                        Extremely Rare

Model No. 1543
CAT - Seated, left front paw up

Designer: Mr. Garbet
Height: Unknown
Colours: Dark pewter (satin gloss)
Issued: 1958-1961

Description: *U.K. £*   *U.S. $*   *Can. $*
Satin gloss   Extremely Rare

Model No. 1558A
SIAMESE CAT - Lying, facing left
Version One -
Puffed out cheeks, short neck, fleshy body

Designer:	Pal Zalmen
Length:	7 1/4", 18.4 cm
Colours:	Chocolate point - gloss
Issued:	1958-c.1963

Description:	*U.K. £*	*U.S. $*	*Can. $*
Chocolate point	95.00	150.00	225.00

Model No. 1558B
SIAMESE CAT - Lying, facing left
Version Two -
Sleek, tapering face, long neck and body

Designer:	Pal Zalmen
Re-modelled:	Albert Hallam
Length:	7 1/4", 18.4 cm
Colours:	1: Seal point - gloss or matt
	2: Copper lustre - gloss
Issued:	1A: Gloss - c.1963-1989
	1B: Matt - 1984-1989
	2: 1971 (export only)

Description:	*U.K. £*	*U.S. $*	*Can. $*
1A: Gloss	40.00	65.00	90.00
1B: Matt	45.00	75.00	100.00
2: Copper lustre	75.00	125.00	150.00

Note: Transferred to R.D. backstamp (DA124) 08/89, in seal point - gloss.

Model No. 1559A
SIAMESE CAT - Lying, facing right
Version One -
Puffed out cheeks, short neck, fleshy body

Designer: Pal Zalmen
Length: 7 1/4", 18.4 cm
Colours: Chocolate point - gloss
Issued: 1958-c1963

Decription:	*U.K. £*	*U.S. $*	*Can. $*
Chocolate point	95.00	150.00	225.00

Model No. 1559B
SIAMESE CAT - Lying, facing right
Version Two -
Sleek, tapering face, long neck and body

Designer: Pal Zalmen
Re-modelled: Albert Hallam
Length: 7 1/4", 18.4 cm
Colours: 1: Seal Point - gloss or matt
               2: Copper lustre - gloss
Issued: 1A: Gloss - c.1963-1989
               1B: Matt - 1984-1989
               2:   Gloss - 1971 (export only)

Description:	*U.K. £*	*U.S. $*	*Can. $*
1A: Gloss	40.00	65.00	90.00
1B: Matt	45.00	75.00	100.00
2: Copper lustre	75.00	125.00	150.00

Note: Transferred to R.D. backstamp (DA125) 08/89, seal point - gloss.

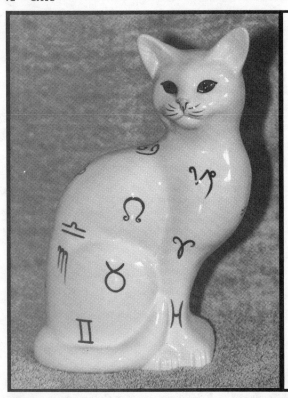

Model No. 1560
ZODIAC CAT - Seated, Facing right

Designer:	Pal Zalmen
Length:	11", 27.9 cm
Colours:	1: Black - gloss
	2: White with zodiac symbols - gloss
Issued:	1958-1967
Set:	Stylised model forming a pair with No. 1561

Description:	U.K. £	U.S. $	Can. $
1: Black	110.00	175.00	275.00
2: White	110.00	175.00	275.00

Photograph not
available at press time

Model No. 1561
ZODIAC CAT - Seated, facing left

Designer:	Pal Zalmen
Length:	11", 27.9 cm
Colours:	1: Black - gloss
	2: White with zodiac symbols - gloss
Issued:	1958-1967
Set:	Stylised model forming a pair with No. 1560

Description:	U.K. £	U.S. $	Can. $
1: Black	110.00	175.00	275.00
2: White	110.00	175.00	275.00

Model No. 1677
SIAMESE CAT - Climbing

Designer:	Albert Hallam
Length:	6 1/2", 16.5 cm
Colours:	Seal point - gloss
Issued:	1960 to the present

Description:	U.K. £	U.S. $	Can. $
Gloss	10.95	N/A	N/A

Model No. 1803
CAT - Seated, looking up

Designer: Albert Hallam
Height: 1 1/4", 3.2 cm
Colours: Ginger stripe - gloss
Issued: 1962-1971
Series: Bedtime Chorus

Description:	U.K. £	U.S. $	Can. $
Gloss	50.00	75.00	100.00

Photograph not
available at press time

Model No. 1857
SIAMESE CAT

Designer: Albert Hallam
Length: 5 1/2", 14.0 cm
Colours: Seal point - gloss
Issued: 1962-Unknown

Description:	U.K. £	U.S. $	Can. $
Probably not put into production.			

Note: Similar in shape to model no. 1677.

Model No. 1867
PERSIAN CAT - Seated, looking up

Designer: Albert Hallam
Height: 8 1/2", 21.6 cm
Colours: 1: Black; White - gloss
2: Ginger; Grey; Grey Swiss roll -gloss
3: Black; Ginger; Grey; White - matt
Issued: 1: 1963-1989
2: 1963-By 1969
3: 1984-1989

Description:	U.K. £	U.S. $	Can. $
1: Black - gloss	55.00	90.00	125.00
1: White - gloss	35.00	55.00	75.00
2: Ginger - gloss	35.00	55.00	75.00
2: Grey - gloss	35.00	55.00	75.00
2: Grey Swiss - gloss	75.00	125.00	175.00
3: Black - matt	45.00	75.00	100.00
3: Ginger - matt	45.00	75.00	100.00
3: Grey - matt	55.00	85.00	125.00
3: White - matt	45.00	75.00	100.00

Note: Transferred to R.D. backstamp (DA126) 08/89,
in ginger, grey and white gloss

Model No. 1876
PERSIAN CAT - Lying

Designer: Albert Hallam
Height: 3 1/2" x 6 1/2", 8. x 6.5 cm
Colours: See below - gloss
Issued: 1963-1971

Description:	U.K. £	U.S. $	Can. $
Ginger	95.00	150.00	225.00
Grey	75.00	125.00	175.00
Grey Swiss roll	95.00	150.00	225.00
Grey stripe	95.00	150.00	225.00
White	75.00	125.00	175.00

Model No. 1880
PERSIAN CAT - Seated, looking up

Designer: Albert Hallam
Height: 5 1/4", 13.3 cm
Colours: See below - gloss
Issued: 1963-1971

Description:	U.K. £	U.S. $	Can. $
Black	110.00	175.00	250.00
Ginger	110.00	175.00	250.00
Grey	75.00	125.00	175.00
Grey Swiss roll	120.00	200.00	275.00
Lead grey	120.00	200.00	275.00
White	95.00	150.00	225.00

Model No. 1877
CAT - Seated, scratching ear

Designer: Albert Hallam
Height: 6 1/2", 16.5 cm
Colours: Black, Ginger; Grey; Grey Swiss roll;
White - gloss
Issued: 1963-1971

Description:	U.K. £	U.S. $	Can. $
Black			
Ginger	95.00	150.00	225.00
Grey	110.00	175.00	250.00
Grey Swiss roll	150.00	225.00	325.00
White	95.00	150.00	225.00

Model No. 1882
SIAMESE CAT - Seated, head forward

Designer:	Albert Hallam
Height:	9 1/2", 24.0 cm
Colours:	1: Copper lustre - gloss
	2: Seal point - gloss or matt
	3: Black - gloss or matt
Issued:	1: Gloss - 1963-1980
	2A: Gloss - 1963-1980
	2B: Matt - 1984-1989
	3A: Gloss - 1986-1989
	3B Matt - 1986-1989
Series:	Fireside Model

Description:	U.K. £	U.S. $	Can. $
1: Copper lustre	125.00	200.00	275.00
2A: Gloss	65.00	100.00	150.00
2B: Matt	75.00	125.00	175.00
3A: Gloss	65.00	100.00	150.00
3B: Matt	75.00	125.00	175.00

Note: Transferred to R.D. backstamp (DA127) 08/89, seal point - gloss.

Model No. 1883
PERSIAN CAT - On hind legs

Designer:	Albert Hallam
Height:	6", 15.0 cm
Colours:	See below - gloss
Issued:	1963-1971

Description:	U.K. £	U.S. $	Can. $
Ginger	85.00	135.00	200.00
Grey	85.00	135.00	200.00
Grey Swiss roll	100.00	150.00	225.00
Lead grey	100.00	150.00	225.00
White	85.00	135.00	200.00

Model No. 1885
PERSIAN KITTEN - Standing

Designer:	Albert Hallam
Height:	4 3/4", 12.1 cm
Colours:	See below - gloss
Issued:	1963-1973

Description:	U.K. £	U.S. $	Can. $
Black	75.00	125.00	165.00
Ginger	75.00	125.00	165.00
Ginger Swiss roll	85.00	135.00	200.00
Grey	75.00	125.00	165.00
Grey Swiss roll	85.00	135.00	200.00
Lead grey	95.00	150.00	225.00
White	75.00	125.00	165.00

Model No 1886
PERSIAN CAT - Seated, looking up

Designer:	Albert Hallam
Height:	4", 10.1 cm
Colours:	Black and White; Ginger; Grey; Grey Swiss roll; White - gloss Ginger; Grey; White - matt
Issued:	Gloss: 1963-1989 Matt: 1984-1989

Description:	U.K. £	U.S. $	Can. $
Black/white - gloss	45.00	75.00	100.00
Ginger - gloss	35.00	55.00	75.00
Ginger - matt	45.00	75.00	100.00
Grey - gloss	35.00	55.00	75.00
Grey - matt	45.00	75.00	100.00
Grey Swiss roll - gloss	55.00	85.00	125.00
White - gloss	35.00	55.00	75.00
White - matt	45.00	75.00	100.00

Note: Transferred to R.D. backstamp (DA128) 08/89, in ginger, grey and white - gloss

Model No. 1887
SIAMESE CAT - Seated, head turned back

Designer:	Albert Hallam
Height:	4", 10.1 cm
Colours:	1: Seal Point - gloss or matt 2: Copper lustre - gloss
Issued:	1A: Gloss - 1971-1989 1B: Matt - 1984-1989 2: Copper Lustre 1971 (export only)

Description:	U.K. £	U.S. $	Can. $
1A: Gloss	15.00	25.00	35.00
1B: Matt	25.00	40.00	55.00
2: Copper lustre	50.00	80.00	115.00

Note: Transferred to R.D. backstamp (DA129) 08/89, in seal point - gloss.

Model No. 1897
SIAMESE CAT - Standing

Designer:	Albert Hallam
Height:	6 1/2", 16.5 cm
Colours:	1: Seal point - gloss and matt
	2: Copper lustre
	3: Black - gloss and matt
Issued:	1A: Gloss - 1963-1980
	1B: Matt - 1984-1989
	2: Copper lustre 1971 (export only)
	3A: Gloss - 1987-1989
	3B: Matt: - 1987-1989
Series:	Fireside Model

Description:	U.K. £	U.S. $	Can. $
1A: Seal Point - (g)	25.00	40.00	55.00
1B: Seal Point - (m)	35.00	55.00	75.00
2: Copper lustre	110.00	175.00	250.00
3A: Black - (g)	35.00	55.00	75.00
3B: Black - (m)	45.00	70.00	100.00

Note: In 1987 introduced as "Lucky Black Cat"..
Transferred to R.D. backstamp 08/89, in
seal point (DA 130) and black (DA131) - gloss.

Model No. 1898
PERSIAN CAT - Standing, tail erect

Designer:	Albert Hallam
Height:	5", 12.7 cm
Colours:	Ginger; Dark ginger; Grey; Lead grey;
	White - gloss
	Black; Ginger; Grey; White - matt
Issued:	Gloss: 1963-1989
	Matt: 1984-1989

Description:	U.K. £	U.S. $	Can. $
Black - matt	20.00	30.00	45.00
Ginger - gloss	25.00	40.00	55.00
Ginger - matt	35.00	55.00	75.00
Dark ginger - gloss	35.00	55.00	75.00
Grey - gloss	25.00	40.00	55.00
Grey - matt	35.00	55.00	75.00
Lead grey - gloss	65.00	100.00	150.00
White - gloss	25.00	40.00	55.00
White - matt	35.00	55.00	75.00

Note: Transferred to R.D. backstamp (DA132) 08/89,
in ginger, grey and white - gloss.

Model No. 2100
CAT WITH MOUSE

Designer:	Albert Hallam
Height:	3", 7.6 cm
Colours:	Brown cat, white mouse - gloss
Issued:	1967-1973
Series:	Fun Models

Description:	U.K. £	U.S. $	Can. $
Gloss	110.00	175.00	250.00

Model No. 2101
CAT - Laughing

Designer:	Albert Hallam
Height:	3", 7.6 cm
Colours:	Grey - gloss
Issued:	1967-1973
Series:	Fun Models

Description:	*U.K. £*	*U.S. $*	*Can. $*
Gloss	100.00	150.00	200.00

Model No. 2139
SIAMESE CAT - Seated, head up

Designer:	Mr. Garbet
Height:	13 3/4", 34.9 cm
Colours:	1: Seal point - gloss
	2: Copper lustre
Issued:	1: 1967-1989
	2: 1971 (export only)
Series:	Fireside Models

Description:	*U.K. £*	*U.S. $*	*Can. $*
1: Gloss	65.00	100.00	150.00
2: Copper lustre	95.00	150.00	225.00

Note: Transferred to R.D. backstamp (DA83) 08/89, in seal point - gloss.

Photograph not
available at press time

Photograph not
available at press time

Model No. 2301
CAT

Designer:	Albert Hallam
Height:	4 1/2", 11.9 cm
Colours:	Unknown
Issued:	1969-Unknown

Description:	*U.K. £*	*U.S. $*	*Can. $*
		Extremely Rare	

Note: Similar to model no. 1677. Possibly not issued.

Model No. 2311
SIAMESE CAT

Designer:	Graham Tongue
Length:	1 1/2", 3.8 cm
Colours:	Unknown
Issued:	1970-Unknown

Description:	*U.K. £*	*U.S. $*	*Can. $*
		Extremely rare	

Note: Similar to model no. 2139. Possibly not issued.

Model No. 2480
CHESHIRE CAT

Designer:	Graham Tongue
Height:	1 1/2", 3.8 cm
Colours:	Tabby - gloss
Issued:	1973-1982
Series:	Alice in Wonderland

Description:	U.K. £	U.S. $	Can. $
Gloss	425.00	650.00	850.00

Note: For the rest of the pieces in the Alice in Wonderland series see the Charlton Standard Catalogue of Royal Doulton Beswick Storybook Figurines.

Model No. 2761
CAT ON CHIMNEY POT

Designer:	Unknown
Height:	4", 10.1 cm
Colours:	White and gold - gloss
Issued:	1982-1986

Description:	U.K. £	U.S. $	Can. $
Gloss	40.00	65.00	90.00

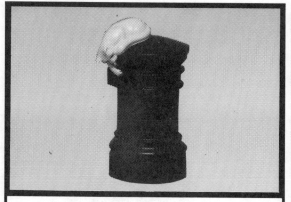

Model No. 2805
CAT ON POST BOX

Designer:	Unknown
Height:	6 1/4", 15.9 cm
Colours:	White cat on red post box - gloss
Issued:	1983-1986

Description:	U.K. £	U.S. $	Can. $
Gloss	55.00	85.00	125.00

Model No. 2810
CAT EGG CUP

Designer:	Unknown
Height:	2 1/2", 6.4 cm
Colours:	Ginger kitten with white egg cup - gloss
Issued:	1983-1986

Description:	U.K. £	U.S. $	Can. $
Gloss	30.00	50.00	65.00

Model No. 2156/2157
CAT CRUET, SALT AND PEPPER

Designer: Unknown
Height: 5 1/2", 14.0 cm
Colours: Black cat (pepper), white cat (salt) - gloss
Issued: 1967-1969

Description:	U.K. £	U.S. $	Can. $
Gloss	35.00	55.00	75.00

Model No. 3012
SPORTING CAT

Designer: Warren Platt
Length: 4 1/4", 10.8 cm
Colours: A: Cat dressed as a soccer player with striped jersey; black, blue, burgundy, red, yellow
B: Cat dressed as a soccer player with plain jersey; black, blue, burgundy, red, yellow
Modelled: 1986
Issued: 1987-1987
Series: Fun Models

Description:	U.K. £	U.S. $	Can. $
Black stripe	45.00	75.00	100.00
Black	45.00	75.00	100.00
Blue stripe			
Blue	45.00	75.00	100.00
Burgundy stripe			
Burgundy	45.00	75.00	100.00
Red stripe			
Red	45.00	75.00	100.00
Yellow stripe			
Yellow	45.00	75.00	100.00

Note: Introduced as a trial in August 1987, but not put into general production, although many sets were sold from the factory shop.

Chapter Four

DOGS

Beswick produced mantlepiece dogs of the old Staffordshire type from about 1898. In 1933, when the shape book was created—in which each model was illustrated by a sketch with details such as height, modeller and dates—these dogs, in various sizes, were the initial numbers. During the 1930s dogs of the novelty type were produced with several unrealistic-looking decorations, including blue and green gloss and mottled blue in a satin-type finish. In fact customers could order novelties in any decoration to match the domestic ware being made at the time. Then in 1941, Arthur Gredington, following his success with realistic models of horses, created the first of the champion dogs, the Dalmatian "Arnoldene," shape number 961. Seven other breeds were also produced in 1941, and four more the following year. These figures were all modelled in a show stance from champions of their particular breed, and almost all of them were modelled by Arthur Gredington.

Over the years most of the popular breeds joined the Beswick "kennel," and many were also produced in a smaller size. Action poses were added to the collection, such as the 1507 Spaniel running. This type of model was reintroduced with the *Good Companions* series in 1987, the same time several more medium-sized dogs were issued. These and the *Good Companions*, had a short production run with the Beswick backstamp (some for less than a year), as from August 1989 they were issued with Royal Doulton backstamps and given DA numbers. By 1994 all the Beswick medium-sized dogs had been withdrawn, leaving only the small dogs collection with Beswick backstamps.

Many of the dogs share with the horses the distinction of being in continual production for four or five decades. During this time there has been a deterioration in the moulds and decorating processes ; therefore, the quality of the models is variable. It is well worth looking out for the older figures that exhibit more mould detail and toning and shading in colour.

The dogs collection also includes some of Beswick's largest models; the seated *Fireside* models range from the 2377 Yorkshire Terrier at 10 1/4" to the 13 1/2" 2314 Labrador. At the other extreme is the tiny 1 1/2" singing dog from the *Bedtime Chorus* set, a very elusive little fellow.

INDEX BY MODEL NUMBER

Photograph Not
available At Press Time

Model Nos. 1 to 6

OLD STAFFORDSHIRE DOGS

Designer: Unknown
Colours: Unknown
Issued: 1933-1955
Series: Mantlepiece Dogs

Model No.	1	2	3	4	5	6
Height:	13 3/4", 34.9 cm	11 1/2", 29.2 cm	10", 25.4 cm	9", 22.9 cm	7 1/2", 19.1 cm	5 1/2", 14.0 cm

Price:	Model No. 1	Model No. 2	Model No. 3	Model No. 4	Model No. 5	Model No. 6
U.K. £	85.00	75.00	65.00	65.00	45.00	35.00
U.S. $	135.00	120.00	100.00	100.00	75.00	55.00
Can. $	190.00	165.00	145.00	145.00	100.00	75.00

Note: Prices above are for singles, they are available in pairs, left and right facing.

Photograph not
available at press time

Model No. 87
DOG SITTING IN ARMCHAIR - Bookend

Designer:	Unknown	
Height:	7", 1.8 cm cm	
Colours:	Unknown	
Issued:	1934-By 1966	
Series:	Fun Models	

Description:	U.K. £	U.S. $	Can. $
	75.00	125.00	160.00

Model No. 88
SCOTTIE - Ashtray

Designer:	Unknown	
Height:	3 1/4", 8.3 cm	
Colours:	Various; Blue - gloss	
Issued:	1934-1965	

Description:	U.K. £	U.S. $	Can. $
1: Various	75.00	110.00	150.00
2: Blue	75.00	110.00	150.00

Model No. 171
DOG - Begging

Designer:	Unknown	
Height:	4 3/4", 12.1 cm	
Colours:	White and tan - gloss	
Issued:	1934-By 1954	

Description:	U.K. £	U.S. $	Can. $
Gloss	75.00	120.00	150.00

Model No. 286
DOG - Seated

Designer:	Mr. Watkin
Height:	6 1/4", 15.9 cm
Colours:	1: White and tan - gloss
	2: Blue - gloss
Issued:	1: 1934-1967
	2: 1934-By 1954

Description:	U.K. £	U.S. $	Can. $
1: White/tan	95.00	150.00	200.00
2: Blue	95.00	150.00	200.00

Model No. 301
SEALYHAM PLAQUE - Bow on right

Designer:	Unknown
Height:	7 1/2", 19.1 cm
Colours:	Cream, blue bow - satin finish
Issued:	1936-1940
Series:	Wall Plaques

Description:	U.K. £	U.S. $	Can. $
Satin finish	95.00	150.00	200.00

Photograph not
available at press time

Model No. 302
SEALYHAM - Standing

Designer:	Mr. Watkin
Height:	6", 15.0 cm
Colours:	1: White with dark ears - gloss
	2: Blue - gloss
Issued:	1: 1936-1967
	2: 1936-By 1964

Description:	U.K. £	U.S. $	Can. $
1: White/dark ears	95.00	200.00	200.00
2: Blue	95.00	250.00	250.00

Model No. 307
SEALYHAM PLAQUE - Bow on left

Designer:	Mr. Watkin
Height:	7", 17.8 cm
Colours:	Cream - satin finish
Issued:	1935-1940
Series:	Wall Plaques

Description:	U.K. £	U.S. $	Can. $
Satin finish	95.00	150.00	200.00

Note: Similar to no. 301, but bow is on left side,
dog's left ear is up and the right ear is down

Model No. 308
PUPPY - Seated

Designer: Mr. Watkin
Height: 6 1/4", 15.9 cm
Colours: 1: White with brown ears - gloss
           2: Blue - gloss
Issued: 1: 1935-1967
           2: 1935-By 1954

Description:	U.K. £	U.S. $	Can. $
1: White/brown	85.00	115.00	200.00
2: Blue	85.00	125.00	225.00

Note: Also issued as a money-box.

Model No. 324
Character Dog - Begging

Designer: Miss Greaves
Height: 7", 17.8 cm
Colours: 1: Unknown - gloss
           2: Blue - gloss
Issued: 1: 1936-By 1954
           2: 1936-By 1954
Series: Fun Models

Description:	U.K. £	U.S. $	Can. $
1: Unknown	95.00	200.00	250.00
2: Blue	95.00	200.00	250.00

Model No. 361
DACHSHUND - Standing

Designer:	Mr. Watkin		
Height:	5 1/2", 14.0 cm		
Colours:	1: Black and tan - gloss		2: Tan - gloss
	3: Blue - gloss		
Issued:	1: 1936-1983		2: 1936-1983
	3: 1936-By-1954		

Description:	U.K. £	U.S. $	Can. $
1: Black / tan	75.00	120.00	160.00
2: Tan	75.00	120.00	160.00
3: Blue	110.00	170.00	275.00

Model No. 453
OLD ENGLISH SHEEPDOG - Seated

Designer:	Unknown	
Height:	8 1/2", 21.6 cm	
Colours:	1: Grey and white - gloss	
	2: Blue - gloss	
Issued:	1: 1936-1973	
	2: 1936-By 1954	

Description:	U.K. £	U.S. $	Can. $
1: Grey / white	110.00	175.00	250.00
2: Blue	125.00	200.00	325.00

Model No. 454
LOLLOPY DOG - Seated Puppy

Designer:	Miss Greaves		
Height:	4 1/4", 10.8 cm		
Colours:	1: Blue - gloss		2: White - gloss
	3: Various, incl. green and		
	orange satin type finish		
Issued:	1: 1936-By 1954		2: 1936-1969
	3: 1936-1969		

Description:	U.K. £	U.S. $	Can. $
1: Blue	75.00	65.00	95.00
2: White	75.00	100.00	125.00
3: Various	75.00	125.00	150.00

Model No. 624
DOG WITH GOLF BAG

Designer:	Miss Catford
Height:	4", 10.1 cm
Colours:	1: Brown and green - gloss
	2: Blue - gloss
Issued:	1: 1938-1967
	2: 1938-By 1954
Series:	Fun Models

Description:	U.K. £	U.S. $	Can. $
1: Brown/green	75.00	120.00	165.00
2: Blue	55.00	85.00	125.00

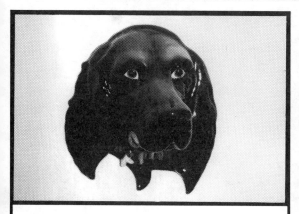

Model No. 668
DOG PLAQUE

Designer: Mr. Symcox
Height: 11", 27.9 cm
Colours: Deep red brown - gloss
Issued: 1938-1960
Series: Wall Plaques

Description:	U.K. £	U.S. $	Can. $
Gloss	175.00	275.00	375.00

Model No. 761
DOG WITH TOOTHACHE

Designer: Mr. Watkin
Height: 4 1/4", 10.8 cm
Colours: White dog with red kerchief
Issued: 1939-1971
Series: Fun Models

Description:	U.K. £	U.S. $	Can. $
Gloss	85.00	135.00	190.00

Photograph not
available at press time

Model No. 804
DOG WITH LADYBIRD ON NOSE

Designer: Mr. Watkin
Height: 4", 10.1 cm
Colours: White with red ladybird - gloss
Issued: 1940-1969
Series: Fun Models

Description:	U.K. £	U.S. $	Can. $
Gloss	150.00	240.00	335.00

Model No. 805
DOG WITH LADYBIRD ON TAIL

Designer: Mr. Watkin
Height: 1: Large - 3 3/4", 9.5 cm
              2: Small - 2 1/2", 6.4 cm
Colours: White dog with red ladybird - gloss
Issued: 1940-1969
Series: Fun Models

Description:	U.K. £	U.S. $	Can. $
1: Large	45.00	80.00	100.00
2: Small	45.00	80.00	100.00

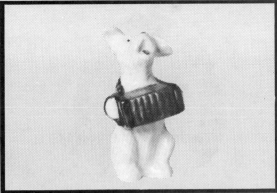

Model No. 810
BULLDOG WITH SAILOR'S HAT - Ashtray

Designer: Arthur Gredington
Height: 4", 10.1 cm
Colours: Unknown
Issued: 1940-1970

Description:	U.K. £	U.S. $	Can. $
	250.00	475.00	500.00

Model No. 811
DOG PLAYING ACCORDIAN

Designer: Mr. Watkin
Height: 4", 10.1 cm
Colours: White dog with green and brown
               accordian - gloss
Issued: 1940-1970

Description:	U.K. £	U.S. $	Can. $
Gloss	50.00	80.00	110.00

Model No. 812
DOG ASLEEP ON DRUM

Designer: Mr. Watkin
Height: 3", 7.6 cm
Colours: White dog, yelow, blue and red
               drum - gloss
Issued: 1940-1970
Series: Fun Models

Description:	U.K. £	U.S. $	Can. $
Gloss	65.00	100.00	150.00

Model No. 813
DOG WITH LADYBIRD ON NOSE

Designer: Mr. Watkin
Height: 4", 10.1 cm
Colours: White dog, red ladybird - gloss
Issued: 1940-1970
Series: Fun Models

Description:	U.K. £	U.S. $	Can. $
Gloss	65.00	100.00	150.00

Model No. 831
DOG WITH GLASSES READING A BOOK

Designer:	Arthur Gredington		
Height:	6 1/4", 15.9 cm		
Colours:	White dog, yellow-red glasses, brown and white book - gloss		
Issued:	1940-1970		
Series:	Fun Models		

Description:	U.K. £	U.S. $	Can. $
Gloss	75.00	125.00	160.00

Model No. 869
FIVE DOG ASHTRAY

Designer:	Mr. Watkin
Height:	2", 5.0 cm
Colours:	1: Brown dog, green ashtray - gloss
	2: Light tan with black shading, green ashtray - gloss
Issued:	1940-1967

Description:	U.K. £	U.S. $	Can. $
1: Brown	45.00	95.00	100.00
2: Light tan	45.00	95.00	100.00

Model No. 907
DOG WITH LADYBIRD ON TAIL

Designer:	Mr. Watkin
Height:	3 3/4", 9.5 cm
Colours:	White dog, red ladybird
Issued:	1941-1971
Series:	Fun Models

Description:	U.K. £	U.S. $	Can. $
Gloss	65.00	100.00	150.00

Model No. 916
THREE DOG ASHTRAY

Designer:	Mr. Watkin
Height:	2", 5.0 cm
Colours:	1: Brown dog, green ashtray - gloss
	2: Light brown with black shading, green ashtray - gloss
Issued:	1941-1967

Description:	U.K. £	U.S. $	Can. $
1: Brown	45.00	75.00	100.00
2: Light brown	45.00	75.00	100.00

Note: The three dogs are same as used in model no. 917.

Model No. 917
THREE DOGS

Designer:	Mr. Watkin
Height:	2", 5.0 cm
Colours:	Brown - gloss
Issued:	1941-1965

Description:	U.K. £	U.S. $	Can. $
Tan - gloss	45.00	75.00	100.00

Note: The three dogs are same as used in model no. 916

Model No. 941
FOXHOUND
Version One - Thick legs and tail

Designer:	Mr. Watkin
Height:	2 3/4", 7.0 cm
Colours:	White, tan and black - gloss
Issued:	1941-1969
Varieties:	2262

Description:	U.K. £	U.S. $	Can. $
Gloss	35.00	50.00	75.00

Note: Remodelled in 1969 see also no. 2263.

Model No. 942
FOXHOUND
Version One - Thick legs and tail

Designer:	Mr. Watkin
Height:	2 3/4", 7.0 cm
Colours:	White, tan and black - gloss
Issued:	1941-1969
Varieties:	2263

Description:	U.K. £	U.S. $	Can. $
Gloss	35.00	50.00	75.00

Note: Remodelled in 1969 see also no. 2263.

Model No. 943
FOXHOUND
Version One - Thick legs and tail

Designer:	Mr. Watkin		
Height:	2 3/4", 7.0 cm		
Colours:	White, tan and black - gloss		
Issued:	1941-1969		
Varieties:	2265		

Description:	U.K. £	U.S. $	Can. $
Gloss	35.00	50.00	75.00

Note: Remodelled in 1969 see also no. 2265.

Model No. 944
FOXHOUND
Version One - Thick legs and tail

Designer:	Mr. Watkin		
Height:	2 3/4", 7.0 cm		
Colours:	White, tan and black - gloss		
Issued:	1941-1969		
Varieties:	2264		

Description:	U.K. £	U.S. $	Can. $
Gloss	35.00	50.00	75.00

Note: Remodelled in 1969 see also no. 2264.

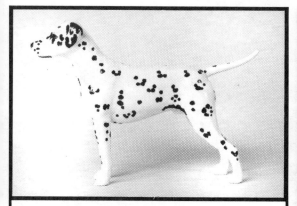

Model No. 961
DALMATION "ARNOLDENE" - Large

Designer:	Arthur Gredington		
Height:	5 3/4", 14.6 cm		
Colours:	White with black spot - gloss; matt		
Issued:	1: Gloss - 1941-1994		
	2: Matt - 1970-1994		

Description:	U.K. £	U.S. $	Can. $
1: Gloss	45.00	70.00	125.00
2: Matt	45.00	70.00	100.00

Note: For the small size see 1763.

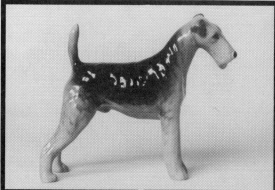

Model No. 962
AIREDALE TERRIER "CAST IRON MONARCH"

Designer:	Arthur Gredington		
Height:	5 1/2", 14.0 cm		
Colours:	Black and tan - gloss; matt		
Issued:	1: Gloss - 1941-1989		
	2: Matt - 1987-1989		

Description:	U.K. £	U.S. $	Can. $
1: Gloss	75.00	125.00	160.00
2: Matt	75.00	125.00	160.00

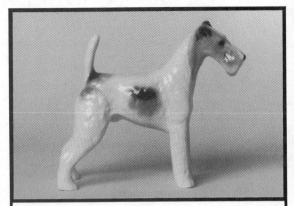

Model No. 963
WIRED-HAIRED TERRIER
"TALAVERA ROMULUS"

Designer: Arthur Gredington
Height: 5 3/4", 14.6 cm
Colours: White, light sandy brown
             and black - gloss
Issued: 1941-1984

Description:	U.K. £	U.S. $	Can. $
Gloss	85.00	150.00	190.00

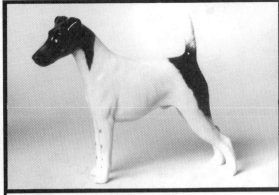

Model No. 964
SMOOTH-HAIRED TERRIER
"ENDON BLACK ROD"

Designer: Arthur Gredington
Height: 5 1/2", 14.0 cm
Colours: White with black patches - gloss
Issued: 1941-1973

Description:	U.K. £	U.S. $	Can. $
Gloss	145.00	295.00	325.00

Model No. 965
BULLDOG "BASFORD BRITISH MASCOT" - Large

Designer: Arthur Gredington
Height: 5 1/2", 14.0 cm
Colours: Brindle, tan and white - gloss; matt
Issued: 1: Gloss - 1941-1990
             2: Matt - 1987-1989

Description:	U.K. £	U.S. $	Can. $
1: Gloss	110.00	150.00	225.00
2: Matt	125.00	175.00	250.00

Note: For small size see no. 1731.

Model No. 966
IRISH SETTER "SUGAR OF WENDOVER"

Designer: Arthur Gredington
Height: 5 3/4", 14.6 cm
Colours: Red brown - gloss; matt
Issued: 1: Gloss - 1941-1989
             2: Matt - 1987-1989

Description:	U.K. £	U.S. $	Can. $
1: Gloss	85.00	125.00	190.00
2: Matt	75.00	120.00	165.00

Model No. 967

COCKER SPANIEL "HORSESHOE PRIMULA"

Designer: Arthur Gredington
Height: 5 3/4",14.6 cm

Colours	Issued	Price U.K. £	U.S. $	Can. $
Golden brown - gloss	1941-1994	30.00	55.00	75.00
Golden brown - matt	1987-1994	25.00	55.00	75.00
Black - gloss	1965-1982	40.00	75.00	75.00
Black and white - gloss	1970-1982	45.00	75.00	75.00
Liver and white - gloss	1970-1994	30.00	55.00	75.00
Liver and white - matt	1987-1994	25.00	55.00	75.00

Model No. 968
GREAT DANE "RULER OF OUBOURGH"

Designer:	Arthur Gredington
Height:	7", 17.8 cm
Colours:	Light sandy brown - gloss; matt
Issued:	1: Gloss - 1941-1994
	2: Matt - 1987-1994

Description:	U.K. £	U.S. $	Can. $
1: Gloss	50.00	95.00	95.00
2: Matt	40.00	80.00	85.00

Model No. 969
ALSATIAN "ULRICA OF BRITTAS" - Large

Designer:	Arthur Gredington
Height:	5 3/4", 14.6 cm
Colours:	Black and light brown - gloss; matt
Issued:	1: 1942-1994
	2: 1970-1994

Description:	U.K. £	U.S. $	Can. $
1: Gloss	50.00	95.00	95.00
2: Matt	40.00	80.00	85.00

Note: For small size see no. 1762.

Model No. 970
BULL TERRIER "ROMANY RHINESTONE" - Large

Designer:	Arthur Gredington
Height:	6 1/2", 16.5 cm
Colours:	1: Brindle and white - gloss
	2: White - gloss; matt
Issued:	1: Gloss - 1942-1975
	2A: Gloss - 1942-1994
	2B: Matt - 1987-1994

Description:	U.K. £	U.S. $	Can. $
1: Brindle/white	100.00	250.00	250.00
2A: White - gloss	50.00	75.00	100.00
2B: White - matt	40.00	75.00	100.00

Model No. 971
SEALYHAM "FORESTEDGE FOXGLOVE"

Designer:	Arthur Gredington
Height:	4 1/4", 10.8 cm
Colours:	White - gloss
Issued:	1942-1967

Description:	U.K. £	U.S. $	Can. $
Gloss	85.00	175.00	195.00

Model No. 972
GREYHOUND "JOVIAL ROGER"

Designer: Arthur Gredington
Height: 6", 15.0 cm
Colours: Light sandy brown - gloss; matt
Issued: 1: Gloss - 1942-1990
2: Matt - 1970-1990

Description:	U.K. £	U.S. $	Can. $
1: Gloss	50.00	95.00	95.00
2: Matt	40.00	80.00	85.00

Model No. 973
ENGLISH SETTER "BAYLDONE BARONET"

Designer: Arthur Gredington
Height: 5 1/2", 14.0 cm
Colours: Speckled grey - gloss; matt
Issued: 1: Gloss - 1942-1989
2: Matt - 1987-1989

Description:	U.K. £	U.S. $	Can. $
1: Gloss	50.00	75.00	95.00
2: Matt	40.00	75.00	85.00

Model No. 1002
PUPPIT DOG

Designer: Arthur Gredington
Height: 4 3/4", 12.1 cm
Colours: White with black markings - gloss
Issued: 1944-1969
Series: Fun Models

Description:	U.K. £	U.S. $	Can. $
Gloss	65.00	100.00	150.00

Model No. 1054
SPANIEL HOLDING "MY PLATE"

Designer: Arthur Gredington
Height: 4 1/4", 12.1 cm
Colours: White and brown - gloss
Issued: 1947-1967
Series: Fun Models

Description:	U.K. £	U.S. $	Can. $
Gloss	75.00	110.00	160.00

Model No. 1055A
CAIRN TERRIER - With ball on left leg

Designer: Arthur Gredington
Height: 4", 10.1 cm
Colours: Beige with brown "stripes', red ball - gloss
Issued: 1946-1969

Description:	U.K. £	U.S. $	Can. $
With ball	95.00	195.00	215.00

Note: Also found with ball on right leg.

Model No. 1055B
CAIRN TERRIER - Without ball

Designer: Arthur Gredington
Height: 4", 10.1 cm
Colours: Beige with brown 'stripes' - gloss
Issued: 1946-1969

Description:	U.K. £	U.S. $	Can. $
Without ball	110.00	195.00	245.00

Model No. 1057
SPANIEL - Running

Designer: Arthur Gredington
Height: 3 3/4", 9.5 cm
Colours: White with golden tan patches - gloss
Issued: 1946-1967

Description:	U.K. £	U.S. $	Can. $
Gloss	75.00	125.00	175.00

Model No. 1058
DOG WITH COLLAR "SCAMP"

Designer: Arthur Gredington
Height: Unknown
Colours: Tan - gloss
Issued: 1948-1973
Seies: Fun Models

Description:	U.K. £	U.S. $	Can. $
Gloss	65.00	100.00	140.00

Model No. 1059
PEKINESE - Begging

Designer: Arthur Gredington
Height: 4 1/4", 10.8 cm
Colours: Golden tan - gloss
Issued: 1946-1967

Description:	U.K. £	U.S. $	Can. $
Gloss	75.00	175.00	165.00

Model No. 1060
RED SETTER - Lying

Designer: Arthur Gredington
Height: 3", 7.6 cm
Colours: Deep red brown - gloss
Issued: 1946-1973

Description:	U.K. £	U.S. $	Can. $
Gloss	65.00	100.00	140.00

Model No. 1061
TERRIER - Lying

Designer:	Arthur Gredington		
Height:	2", 5.0 cm		
Colours:	White with light tan patches - gloss		
Issued:	1946-1973		

Description:	*U.K. £*	*U.S. $*	*Can. $*
Gloss	95.00	175.00	200.00

Model No. 1062
TERRIER - Walking

Designer:	Arthur Gredington		
Height:	4", 10.1 cm		
Colours:	White with light tan and black patches - gloss		
Issued:	1946-1973		

Description:	*U.K. £*	*U.S. $*	*Can. $*
Gloss	75.00	150.00	175.00

Model No. 1088
COMICAL DACHSHUND

Designer:	Miss Jones		
Height:	3 1/2", 8.9 cm		
Colours:	White and brown - gloss		
Issued:	1947-1973		
Series:	Fun Models		

Description:	*U.K. £*	*U.S. $*	*Can. $*
Gloss	65.00	100.00	140.00

Model No. 1202
BOXER "BLUE MOUNTAIN GRETA" - Large

Designer:	Arthur Gredington		
Height:	5 1/2", 14.0 cm		
Colours:	1: Brindle - gloss; matt		
	2: Tan - gloss		
Issued:	1A: Gloss - 1950-1989		
	1B: Matt - 1987-1989		
	2: Gloss - 1973-1975		

Description:	*U.K. £*	*U.S. $*	*Can. $*
1A: Brindle - gloss	55.00	75.00	95.00
1B: Brindle - matt	65.00	75.00	95.00
2 Tan - gloss	75.00	95.00	125.00

Model No. 1220
ENGLISH SETTER

Designer: Arthur Gredington
Height: 8", 20.3 cm
Colours: Speckled grey - gloss
Issued: 1951-1973

Description:	U.K. £	U.S. $	Can. $
Gloss	225.00	450.00	500.00

Model No. 1239
DOG WITH RUFF - Begging

Designer: Arthur Gredington
Height: 2 1/2", 6.4 cm
Colours: White and light tan - gloss
Issued: 1952-1967

Description:	U.K. £	U.S. $	Can. $
Gloss	65.00	125.00	150.00

Note: Originally issued in combination as model no. 1086 "Clown and Dog".

Model No. 1240
DOG - Seated

Designer: Arthur Gredington
Height: 2", 5.0 cm
Colours: White and light tan - gloss
Issued: 1952-1952

Description:	U.K. £	U.S. $	Can. $
Gloss	75.00	125.00	160.00

Note: Originally produced in combination as model no. 1096 "Sportsman".

Model No. 1241
DOG - Howling

Designer: Arthur Gredington
Height: 1 1/4", 3.2 cm
Colours: White and light tan - gloss
Issued: 1952-1952

Description:	U.K. £	U.S. $	Can. $
Gloss	75.00	125.00	160.00

Note: Originally produced in combination as model no. 909 "Puppy Love" (Hummel 1)

Model No. 1242
DOG - Barking

Designer:	Arthur Gredington
Height:	1 1/4", 3.2 cm
Colours:	White and light tan - gloss
Issued:	1952-1952

Description:	U.K. £	U.S. $	Can. $
Gloss	75.00	125.00	160.00

Note: Originally issued in combination as model no. 906 "Strolling Along" (Hummel 5).

Model No. 1294
POODLE "EBONIT AV BARBETT"

Designer:	Arthur Gredington
Height:	5 3/4", 14.0 cm
Colours:	1: Black - gloss
	2: White - gloss
Issued:	1: 1953-1967
	2: 1953-1967

Description:	U.K. £	U.S. $	Can. $
1: Black	150.00	200.00	250.00
2: White	150.00	200.00	250.00

Model No. 1299A
CORGI "BLACK PRINCE" - Large

Designer:	Arthur Gredington
Height:	5 1/2",14.0 cm
Colours:	Black, tan and white - gloss
Issued:	1953-1982
Varieties:	1299B

Description:	U.K. £	U.S. $	Can. $
Gloss	75.00	150.00	175.00

Note: For small size see no. 1736.

Model No. 1299B
CORGI - Large

Designer:	Arthur Gredington
Height:	5 1/2",14.0 cm
Colours:	1: Golden brown - gloss
	2: Golden brown - matt
Issued:	1: 1953-1994
	2: 1987-1994
Varieties:	1299A

Description:	U.K. £	U.S. $	Can. $
1: Gloss	55.00	75.00	90.00
2: Matt	50.00	70.00	80.00

Note: For small size see no. 1736.

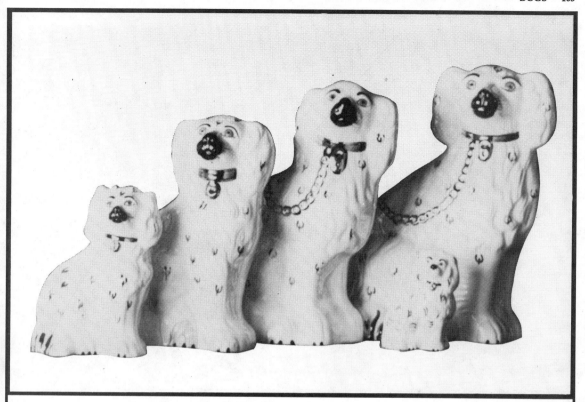

Model No. 1378

OLD ENGLISH DOGS
Left and right facing pairs

Designer: Unknown
Series: Mantlepiece Dogs

Colourways	Height	Issued	U.K. £	Price U.S. $	Can. $
Red and gold - gloss	13 1/4"	1955-1973	100.00	.00	.00
White and gold - gloss	13 1/4"	1955-1976	80.00	.00	.00
Red and Gold - gloss	11 1/2"	1955-1972	90.00	.00	.00
White and gold - gloss	11 1/2"	1955-1972	80.00	.00	.00
Red and gold - gloss	10"	1955-1973	80.00	.00	.00
White and gold - gloss	10"	1955-1989	55.00	.00	.00
Red and gold - gloss	9"	1955-1973	70.00	.00	.00
White and gold - gloss	9"	1955-1989	35.00	.00	.00
Red and gold - gloss	7 1/2",	1955-1973	50.00	.00	.00
White and gold - gloss	7 1/2",	1955-1989	25.00	.00	.00
Red and Gold - gloss	5 1/2", 14.0 cm	1955-1973	40.00	.00	.00
White and gold - gloss	5 1/2", 14.0 cm	1955-1989	20.00	.00	.00
Red and gold - gloss	3 1/2", 8.9 cm	1955-1973	30.00	.00	.00
White and gold - gloss	3 1/2", 8.9 cm	1955-1989	12.00	.00	.00

Note: Transferred to R.D. backstamp (DA89-98) 08/89.

Model No. 1386

POODLE

Designer: Arthur Gredington
Height: 3 1/2", 8.9 cm

Colours	Issued	U.K. £	Price U.S. $	Can. $
Brown - gloss	1953-1973	45.00	75.00	95.00
Black - gloss	1955-1990	40.00	55.00	45.00
Black - matt	1988-1989	55.00	55.00	45.00
White - gloss	1955-1990	35.00	55.00	45.00
White - matt	1984-1989	35.00	55.00	45.00

Model No. 1460
DACHSHUND - Seated

Designer: Arthur Gredington
Height: 2 3/4", 7.0 cm
Colours: 1: Black and tan - gloss or matt
2: Tan - gloss or matt
Issued: 1A: Gloss - 1956 to the present
1B: Matt - 1984-1989
2A: Gloss - 1956-1990
2B: Matt - 1984-1990

Description:	U.K. £	U.S. $	Can. $
1A: Gloss	9.95	N/A	N/A
1B: Matt	20.00	35.00	45.00
2A: Tan - gloss	20.00	35.00	65.00
2B: Tan - matt	20.00	35.00	55.00

Model No. 1461
DACHSHUND - Begging

Designer: Arthur Gredington
Height: 4", 10.1 cm
Colours: 1: Tan - gloss
2: Black and tan - gloss
Issued: 1: 1957-1975
2: 1957-1980

Description:	U.K. £	U.S. $	Can. $
1: Tan	65.00	95.00	100.00
2: Black and tan	60.00	75.00	85.00

Model No. 1548

LABRADOR "SOLOMON OF WENDOVER"- Large

Designer: Arthur Gredington
Height: 5 1/2", 14.0 cm

Colours	Issued	U.K. £	Price U.S. $	Can. $
Golden yellow - gloss	1958-1994	35.00	65.00	75.00
Golden yellow - matt	1970-1994	30.00	65.00	65.00
Black - gloss	1958-1994	35.00	65.00	75.00
Black - matt	1987-1994	30.00	65.00	65.00

Note: For small size see no. 1956.

Model No. 1731
BULLDOG "BOSUN" - Small

Designer:	Unknown
Height:	2 1/2", 6.4 cm
Colours:	Tan and white - gloss; matt
Issued:	1: Gloss - 1960 to the present
	2: Matt - 1984-1989

Description:	U.K. £	U.S. $	Can. $
1: Gloss	11.50	N/A	N/A
2: Matt	15.00	25.00	30.00

Note: For large size see no. 965.

Model No. 1736
CORGI - Small

Designer:	Unknown
Height:	2 3/4", 7.0 cm
Colours:	Golden brown - gloss; matt
Issued:	1: Gloss - 1961 to the present
	2: Matt - 1984-1989

Description:	U.K. £	U.S. $	Can. $
1: Gloss	9.95	N/A	N/A
2: Matt	15.00	25.00	30.00

Note: For large size see no. 1299.

Photograph not
available at press time

Model No. 1738
PUP WITH BONE

Designer:	Harry Sales
Height:	3 3/4", 9.5 cm
Colours:	White - gloss
Issued:	1961-1967
Series:	Fun Models

Description:	U.K. £	U.S. $	Can. $
Gloss	100.00	160.00	225.00

Model No. 1753
BULL TERRIER - Small

Designer:	Arthur Gredington
Height:	3 1/2", 8.9 cm
Colours:	White with bright tan patches - gloss
Issued:	1961-1971

Description:	U.K. £	U.S. $	Can. $
Gloss	75.00	150.00	165.00

Note: For large size see no. 970.

Model No. 1754

COCKER SPANIEL

Designer: Arthur Gredington
Height: 3", 7.6 cm

Colours	Issued	U.K. £	Price U.S. $	Can. $
Black and white - gloss	1961 to the present	11.50	N/A	N/A
Black and white - matt	1984-1989	15.00	45.00	45.00
Liver and white - gloss	1961 to the present	11.50	N/A	N/A
Liver and white - matt	1984-1989	15.00	45.00	45.00

Model No. 1762A
ALSATIAN
First Version - 'Wolf-like', tail not fully attached to leg

Designer:	Mr. Garbet		
Height:	3 1/4", 8.3 cm		
Colours:	Black and cream - gloss		
Issued:	1961-1963		

Description:	*U.K. £*	*U.S. $*	*Can. $*
Gloss	45.00	70.00	100.00

Model No. 1762B
ALSATIAN - Small
Verson Two - 'Fine head', tail attached to leg

Designer:	Arthur Gredington		
Height:	3 1/4",8.3 cm		
Colours:	Black and cream - gloss		
Issued:	1963-1966		

Description:	*U.K. £*	*U.S. $*	*Can. $*
Gloss	35.00	55.00	75.00

Note: For large size see no. 969.

Model No. 1763
DALMATION - Small

Designer:	Mr. Garbet		
Height:	3 1/2", 8.9 cm		
Colours:	White with black spots - gloss; matt		
Issued:	1: Gloss - 1961 to the present		
	2: Matt - 1984-1989		

Description:	*U.K. £*	*U.S. $*	*Can. $*
1: Gloss	11.50	N/A	N/A
2: Matt	15.00	45.00	45.00

Note: For large size see no. 961.

Model No. 1786A
WHIPPET "WINGED FOOT MARKSMAN OF ALLWAYS"
First Version - Tail curls between legs

Designer:	Arthur Gredington		
Height:	4 1/2", 11.9 cm		
Colours:	Light sandy brown - gloss		
Issued:	1961-Unknown		

Description:	*U.K. £*	*U.S. $*	*Can. $*
Gloss	95.00	150.00	200.00

Model No. 1786B
WHIPPET "WINGED FOOT MARKSMAN OF ALLWAYS"
Second Version - Tail attached to leg

Designer:	Arthur Gredington
Height:	4 1/2", 11.9 cm
Colours:	Light sandy brown - gloss; matt
Issued:	1: Gloss - Unknown-1989
	2: Matt - 1987-1989

Description:	U.K. £	U.S. $	Can. $
1: Gloss	45.00	75.00	90.00
2: Matt	40.00	55.00	75.00

Model No. 1791
COLLIE "LOCHINVAR OF LADYPARK" - Large

Designer:	Arthur Gredington
Height:	5 3/4", 14.6 cm
Colours:	Golden brown and white - gloss; matt
Issued:	1: Gloss - 1961-1994
	2: Matt - 1970-1994

Description:	U.K. £	U.S. $	Can. $
1: Gloss	35.00	55.00	75.00
2: Matt	30.00	45.00	65.00

Note: For small size see no. 1814

Model No. 1792
SHEEPDOG - Large

Designer:	Arthur Gredington
Height:	5 1/2", 14.0 cm
Colours:	1: Black and white - gloss; matt
Issued:	1: Gloss - 1961-1994
	2: Matt - 1987-1994

Description:	U.K. £	U.S. $	Can. $
1: Gloss	35.00	55.00	75.00
2: Matt	30.00	45.00	65.00

Note: For small size see no. 1854.

Model No. 1814
COLLIE - Small

Designer:	Arthur Gredington
Height:	3 1/4", 8.3 cm
Colours:	Golden brown and white
Issued:	1962-1975

Description:	U.K. £	U.S. $	Can. $
Gloss	40.00	95.00	90.00

Note: For large size see no. 1791.

Model No. 1824
DOG - Singing

Designer:	Albert Hallam
Height:	1 1/2", 3.8 cm
Colours:	Tan - gloss
Issued:	1962-1971
Series:	Bedtime Chorus

Description:	U.K. £	U.S. $	Can. $
Gloss	45.00	70.00	90.00

Model No. 1852
BOXER - Small

Designer:	Arthur Gredington
Height:	3", 7.6 cm
Colours:	Tan - gloss
Issued:	1962-1975

Description:	U.K. £	U.S. $	Can. $
Gloss	40.00	65.00	90.00

Note: For large size see no. 1202.

Model No. 1854
SHEEPDOG - Small

Designer:	Arthur Gredington
Height:	3", 7.6 cm
Colours:	1: Black and white - gloss; matt
Issued:	1: Gloss - 1962 to the present
	2: Matt - 1987-1989

Description:	U.K. £	U.S. $	Can. $
1: Gloss	11.50	N/A	N/A
2: Matt	15.00	25.00	30.00

Note: For large size see no. 1792.

Model No. 1855
RETRIEVER

Designer:	Arthur Gredington
Height:	3 1/4", 8.3 cm
Colours:	Light golden brown - gloss
Issued:	1962-1975

Description:	U.K. £	U.S. $	Can. $
Gloss	50.00	75.00	95.00

Model No. 1871
POODLE

Designer:	Arthur Gredington
Height:	4 1/4", 10.8 cm
Colours:	White, red bow - gloss
Issued:	1963-1967
Series:	Advertising ware "Dubonnet"

Description:	U.K. £	U.S. $	Can. $
Gloss	85.00	135.00	175.00

Model No. 1872
BULLDOG

Designer:	Arthur Gredington
Height:	3 3/4", 9.5 cm
Colours:	White, pale tan ear and round eyes - gloss
Issued:	1963-1967
Series:	Advertising ware "Dubonnet"

Description:	U.K. £	U.S. $	Can. $
Gloss	75.00	120.00	165.00

Model No. 1918
ASHTRAY WITH DOG

Designer:	Albert Hallam
Height:	11" x 8", 27.9 x 20.3 cm
Colours:	Pale brown - gloss
Issued:	1963-1972

Description:	U.K. £	U.S. $	Can. $
Gloss	65.00	150.00	150.00

Note: This ashtray was available with any small dog attached to it. Model shown is no. 1762.

Model No. 1932
DACHSHUND - Ashtray

Designer:	Albert Hallam
Height:	5", 12.7 cm
Colours:	1: Black and tan - gloss
	2: Tan - gloss
Issued:	1962-1969

Description:	U.K. £	U.S. $	Can. $
1: Black/tan	75.00	150.00	150.00
2: Tan	75.00	150.00	150.00

Model No. 1933A
BEAGLE "WENDOVER BILLY" - Large

Designer:	Arthur Gredington
Height:	5 1/2", 14.0 cm
Colours:	Black, tan and white - gloss or matt
Issued:	1: 1964-1989
	2: 1987-1989
Varieties:	1933B

Description:	U.K. £	U.S. $	Can. $
1: Gloss	40.00	65.00	90.00
2: Matt	35.00	55.00	75.00

Note: For small size see no. 1939.

Model No. 1933B
BEAGLE "WENDOVER BILLY" - on wooden plinth

Designer:	Arthur Gredington
Height:	6", 15.0 cm
Colours:	Black, tan and white - matt
Issued:	1970-1989
Series:	Connoisseur Dogs
Varieties:	1933A

Description:	U.K. £	U.S. $	Can. $
Matt	60.00	95.00	135.00

Model No. 1939
BEAGLE "WENDOVER BILLY" - Small

Designer:	Arthur Gredington
Height:	3", 7.6 cm
Colours:	Black, tan and white - gloss or matt
Issued:	1: Gloss - 1964 to the present
	2: Matt- -1984-1989

Description:	U.K. £	U.S. $	Can. $
1: Gloss	11.50	N/A	N/A
2: Matt	15.00	25.00	30.00

Note: For large size see no. 1933A.

Model No. 1944
YORKSHIRE TERRIER - Lying

Designer:	Arthur Gredington
Height:	3 1/2", 8.9 cm
Colours:	Grey and tan - gloss
Issued:	1964-1976

Description:	U.K. £	U.S. $	Can. $
Gloss	65.00	125.00	135.00

Model No. 1956

LABRADOR - Small

Designer: Arthur Gredington
Height: 3 1/4", 8.3 cm

Colours	Isued	U.K. £	Price U.S. $	Can. $
Black - gloss	1964 to the present	9.95	N/A	N/A
Black - matt	1984-1989	15.00	25.00	20.00
Golden brown - gloss	1964 to the present	9.95	N/A	N/A
Golden brown - matt	1984-1989	15.00	25.00	30.00

Note: For large size see no. 1548.

Model No. 1982A
STAFFORDSHIRE BULL TERRIER
"BANDITS BRINTIGA"

Designer:	Arthur Gredington
Height:	4 3/4", 12.1 cm
Colours:	Dark brindle - gloss
Issued:	1964-1969

Description:	U.K. £	U.S. $	Can. $
Gloss	95.00	160.00	225.00

Model No. 1982B
STAFFORDSHIRE BULL TERRIER

Designer:	Arthur Gredington
Height:	4 3/4", 12.1 cm
Colours:	Tan and white - gloss
Issued:	1964-1969

Description:	U.K. £	U.S. $	Can. $
Gloss	95.00	160.00	225.00

Model No. 1990
OLD ENGLISH SHEEPDOG

Designer:	Mr. Mortimer
Height:	12 1/2", 31.7 cm
Colours:	Black, grey and white - gloss
Issued:	1964-1970
Series:	Advertising ware "Dulux"

Description:	U.K. £	U.S. $	Can. $
Gloss	300.00	475.00	675.00

Model No. 1997
PUG "CUTMIL CUTIE" - Large

Designer:	Arthur Gredington
Height:	4 1/2", 11.9 cm
Colours:	Light sandy brown - gloss or matt
Issued:	1: Gloss - 1965-1982
	2: Matt - 1970-1982

Description:	U.K. £	U.S. $	Can. $
1: Gloss	75.00	125.00	160.00
2: Matt	70.00	100.00	150.00

Model No. 1998
PUG - Small

Designer:	Arthur Gredington
Height:	2 1/2", 6.4 cm
Colours:	Light sandy brown - gloss or matt
Issued:	1: Gloss - 1966-1990
	2: Matt - 1984-1989

Description:	U.K. £	U.S. $	Can. $
1: Gloss	60.00	55.00	100.00
2: Matt	60.00	55.00	100.00

Model No. 2023
JACK RUSSELL TERRIER - Large

Designer:	Arthur Gredington
Height:	5", 12.7 cm
Colours:	White body, tan/black head - gloss or matt
Issued:	1: Gloss - 1965-1994
	2: Matt - 1987-1994

Description:	U.K. £	U.S. $	Can. $
1: Gloss	35.00	75.00	75.00
2: Matt	35.00	75.00	75.00

Note: For small size see no. 2109.

Model No. 2037
SCOTTIE

Designer:	Arthur Gredington
Height:	4 1/2", 11.9 cm
Colours:	Black - gloss or matt
Issued:	1: Gloss - 1965-1990
	2: Matt - 1987-1989

Description:	U.K. £	U.S. $	Can. $
1: Gloss	35.00	55.00	75.00
2: Matt	30.00	45.00	65.00

Model No. 2038
WEST HIGHLAND TERRIER

Designer: Arthur Gredington
Height: 4 3/4", 12.1 cm
Colours: White - gloss or matt
Issued: 1: Gloss - 1965-1994
             2: Matt - 1987-1989

Description:	U.K. £	U.S. $	Can. $
1: Gloss	45.00	85.00	95.00
2: Matt	45.00	85.00	95.00

Model No. 2045A
BASSET HOUND "FOCHNO TRINKET"

Designer: Arthur Gredington
Height: 5", 12.7 cm
Colours: Black, white and tan - gloss or matt
Issued: 1: Gloss - 1965-1994
             2: Matt - 1987-1994

Description:	U.K. £	U.S. $	Can. $
1: Gloss	45.00	75.00	95.00
2: Matt	45.00	75.00	95.00

Photograph not
available at press time

Model No. 2045B
BASSET HOUND "FOCHNO TRINKET"
- on wooden plinth

Designer: Arthur Gredington
Height: 6", 15.0 cm
Colours: Black white and tan - matt
Issued: 1970-1989
Series: Connoisseur Dogs

Description:	U.K. £	U.S. $	Can. $
Matt	75.00	150.00	150.00

Model No. 2102
YORKSHIRE TERRIER LAUGHING

Designer: Albert Halam
Height: 3", 7.6 cm
Colours: Tan - gloss
Issued: 1967-1972
Series: Fun Models

Description:	U.K. £	U.S. $	Can. $
Gloss	60.00	95.00	135.00

Model No. 2107A
KING CHARLES SPANIEL "BLENHEIM"

Designer: Arthur Gredington
Height: 5 1/4", 13.3 cm
Colours: Tan and white - gloss or matt
Issued: 1: Gloss - 1967-1994
            2: Matt - 1987-1994

Description:	U.K. £	U.S. $	Can. $
1: Gloss	45.00	75.00	95.00
2: Matt	45.00	75.00	95.00

Model No. 2107B
KING CHARLES SPANIEL
"JOSEPHINE OF BLAGREAVES"

Designer: Arthur Gredington
Height: 5 1/4", 13.3 cm
Colours: Black, tan and white - gloss or matt
Issued: 1: Gloss - 1967-1994
            2: Matt - 1987-1994

Description:	U.K. £	U.S. $	Can. $
1: Gloss	45.00	75.00	95.00
2: Matt	45.00	75.00	95.00

Model No. 2108
POODLE "IVANOLA GOLD DIGGER"

Designer: Arthur Gredington
Height: 5 3/4", 14.6 cm
Colours: White, blue bow - gloss
Issued: 1967-1971

Description:	U.K. £	U.S. $	Can. $
Gloss	150.00	240.00	335.00

Model No. 2109
JACK RUSSELL TERRIER - Small

Designer: Arthur Gredington and
            Albert Hallam
Height: 2 1/2", 6.4 cm
Colours: White with tan head - gloss or matt
Issued: 1: Gloss - 1967 to the present
            2: Matt - 1984-1989

Description:	U.K. £	U.S. $	Can. $
1: Gloss	11.50	N/A	N/A
2: Matt	15.00	25.00	30.00

Note: For large size see no. 2023.

Model No. 2112
CAIRN TERRIER

Designer:	Arthur Gredington and
	Albert Hallam
Height:	2 3/4", 7.0 cm
Colours:	Dark cream - gloss or matt
Issued:	1: Gloss - 1967 to the present
	2: Matt - 1984-1989

Description:	U.K. £	U.S. $	Can. $
1: Gloss	9.95	N/A	N/A
2: Matt	15.00	25.00	30.00

Model No. 2130
DOG PRAYING

Designer:	Albert Hallam
Height:	3", 7.6 cm
Colours:	Blue - gloss
Issued:	1967-1972
Series:	Fun Models

Description:	U.K. £	U.S. $	Can. $
Gloss	65.00	100.00	145.00

Model No. 2221
ST. BERNARD "CORNA GARTH STROLLER"

Designer:	Albert Hallam
Height:	5 1/2", 14.0 cm
Colours:	Dark brown, tan and white - gloss or matt
Issued:	1: Gloss - 1968-1989
	2: Matt - 1970-1989

Description:	U.K. £	U.S. $	Can. $
1: Gloss	65.00	100.00	125.00
2: Matt	65.00	100.00	125.00

Model No. 2232
OLD ENGLISH SHEEPDOG

Designer:	Albert Hallam
Height:	11 1/2", 29.2 cm
Colours:	Grey and white - gloss
Issued:	1968-1989
Series:	Fireside Models

Description:	U.K. £	U.S. $	Can. $
Gloss	95.00	185.00	225.00

Note: Transferred to the R.D. backstamp (DA84) 08/89.

Model No. 2235
BASSETHOUND - Wall Mask

Designer: Graham Tongue
Height: 6 1/4" x 4 1/2", 15.9 x 11.9 cm (concave)
Colours: Tan and white head, - gloss
               black satin surround
Issued: c.1970-c.1975
Series: Wall Masks

Description:	U.K. £	U.S. $	Can. $
	65.00	100.00	145.00

Model No. 2262
FOXHOUND
Version Two - Thin legs and tail

Designer: Graham Tongue
Height: 2 1/2", 6.4 cm
Colours: White, tan and black - gloss or matt
Issued: 1: Gloss - 1969 to the present
               2: Matt - 1984-1989
Varieties: 941

Description:	U.K. £	U.S. $	Can. $
1: Gloss	8.75	N/A	N/A
2: Matt	15.00	30.00	45.00

Model No. 2263
FOXHOUND
Version Two - Thin legs and tail

Designer: Graham Tongue
Height: 3", 7.6 cm
Colours: White, tan and black - gloss or matt
Issued: 1: Gloss - 1969 to the present
               2: Matt - 1984-1989
Varieties: 942

Description:	U.K. £	U.S. $	Can. $
1: Gloss	8.75	N/A	N/A
2: Matt	15.00	30.00	45.00

Model No. 2264
FOXHOUND
Version Two - Thin legs and tail

Designer:	Graham Tongue
Height:	3", 7.6 cm
Colours:	White, tan and black - gloss or matt
Issued:	1: Gloss - 1969 to the present
	2: Matt - 1984-1989
Varieties:	944

Description:	U.K. £	U.S. $	Can. $
1: Gloss	8.75	N/A	N/A
2: Matt	15.00	30.00	45.00

Model No. 2265
FOXHOUND
Version Two - Thin legs and tail

Designer:	Graham Tongue
Height:	2 3/4", 7.0 cm
Colours:	White, tan and black - gloss or matt
Issued:	1: Gloss - 1969 to the present
	2: Matt - 1984-1989
Varieties:	943

Description:	U.K. £	U.S. $	Can. $
1: Gloss	8.75	N/A	N/A
2: Matt	15.00	30.00	45.00

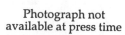

Photograph not
available at press time

Model No. 2268
POODLE - Wall Mask

Designer:	Graham Tongue
Height:	Unknown (Concave)
Colours:	Unknown
Issued:	c.1970-c.1975
Series:	Wall Masks

Description:	U.K. £	U.S. $	Can. $
	65.00	100.00	145.00

Model No. 2271
DALMATIAN

Designer:	Graham Tongue
Height:	13 3/4", 34.9 cm
Colours:	White with black spots - gloss
Issued:	1969-1989
Series:	Fireside Models

Description:	U.K. £	U.S. $	Can. $
White/black	75.00	185.00	200.00

Note: Transferred to R.D.backstamp (DA85) 08/89.

Model No. 2285
AFGHAN HOUND "HAJUBAH OF DAVIEN"

Designer:	Graham Tongue
Height:	5 1/2", 14.0 cm
Colours:	Golden and dark brown - gloss or matt
Issued:	1: Gloss - 1969-1994
	2: Matt - 1987-1989

Description:	U.K. £	U.S. $	Can. $
1: Gloss	55.00	75.00	115.00
2: Matt	65.00	85.00	125.00

Model No. 2286
DACHSHUND

Designer:	Albert Hallam
Height:	10 1/2", 26.7 cm
Colours:	1: Black and tan - gloss
	2: Tan - gloss
Issued:	1: 1969-1981
	2: 1969-1981
Series:	Fireside Models

Description:	U.K. £	U.S. $	Can. $
1: Black/Tan	110.00	185.00	225.00
2: Tan	110.00	185.00	225.00

Model No. 2287
GOLDEN RETRIEVER "CABUS CADET"

Designer:	Graham Tongue
Height:	5 1/2", 14.0 cm
Colours:	Light golden brown - gloss or matt
Issued:	1: Gloss - 1969-1994
	2: Matt - 1987-1994

Description:	U.K. £	U.S. $	Can. $
1: Gloss	55.00	75.00	115.00
2: Matt	65.00	85.00	125.00

Model No. 2299
DOBERMAN PINSCHER "ANNASTOCK LANCE"

Designer:	Graham Tongue
Height:	5 3/4", 14.6 cm
Colours:	Black and tan - gloss or matt
Issued:	1: Gloss - 1970-1994
	2: Matt - 1987-1994

Description:	U.K. £	U.S. $	Can. $
1: Gloss	55.00	75.00	115.00
2: Matt	65.00	85.00	125.00

Model No. 2300
BEAGLE

Designer: Albert Hallam
Height: 12 3/4", 32.4 cm
Colours: Black, tan and white - gloss
Issued: 1969-1983
Series: Fireside Models

Description:	U.K. £	U.S. $	Can. $
Gloss	150.00	225.00	300.00

Model No. 2314
LABRADOR

Designer: Graham Tongue
Height: 13 1/2", 34.3 cm
Colours: 1: Golden brown - gloss
2: Black - gloss
Issued: 1970-1989
Series: Fireside Models

Description:	U.K. £	U.S. $	Can. $
1: Golden brown	110.00	185.00	225.00
2: Black	110.00	185.00	225.00

Note: Transferred to R.D. back stamp (DA 86) 08/89.

Model No. 2339
POODLE

Designer: Graham Tongue
Height: 5 3/4", 14.6 cm
Colours: 1: Black - gloss
2: White - gloss
Issued: 1971-1983

Description:	U.K. £	U.S. $	Can. $
1: Black	15.00	25.00	35.00
2: White	15.00	25.00	35.00

Model No. 2377
YORKSHIRE TERRIER

Designer:	Graham Tongue
Height:	10 1/4", 26.0 cm
Colours:	Grey and tan - gloss
Issued:	1971-1989
Series:	Fireside Models

Description:	U.K. £	U.S. $	Can. $
Gloss	110.00	185.00	225.00

Note: Transferred to R.D. backstamp (DA87) 08/89.

Model No. 2410
ALSATIAN

Designer:	Graham Tongue
Height:	14", 35.5 cm
Colours:	Dark and sandy brown - gloss
Issued:	1972-1989
Series:	Fireside Models

Description:	U.K. £	U.S. $	Can. $
Gloss	110.00	185.00	225.00

Note: Transferred to R.D. backstamp (DA88) 08/89.

Model No. 2448
LAKELAND TERRIER

Designer:	Albert Hallam
Height:	3 1/4", 8.3 cm
Colours:	Pale tan and black - gloss or matt
Issued:	1: Gloss - 1973 to the present
	2: Matt - 1984-1989

Description:	U.K. £	U.S. $	Can. $
1: Gloss	9.95	N/A	N/A
2: Matt	15.00	45.00	45.00

Model No. 2454
CHIHUAHUA - Lying on cushion

Designer:	Albert Hallam
Height:	2 3/4", 7.0 cm
Colours:	Cream dog, maroon cushion - gloss or matt
Issued:	1: 1973 to the present
	2: 1984-1989

Description:	U.K. £	U.S. $	Can. $
1: Gloss	11.50	N/A	N/A
2: Matt	15.00	25.00	45.00

Model No. 2581
COLLIE - on wooden plinth

Designer:	Graham Tongue	
Height:	8", 20.3 cm	
Colours:	Golden brown and white - matt	
Issued:	1979-1989	
Series:	Connoisseur Dogs	

Description:	U.K. £	U.S. $	Can. $
Matt	95.00	150.00	200.00

Note: Transferred to R.D. backstamp (DA24) 08/89.

Model No. 2587
ALSATIAN - on wooden plinth

Designer:	Graham Tongue	
Height:	9", 22.9 cm	
Colours:	Dark and sandy brown - matt	
Issued:	1979-1989	
Series:	Connoisseur Dogs	

Description:	U.K. £	U.S. $	Can. $
Matt	95.00	150.00	200.00

Note: Transferred to R.D. backstamp (DA26) 08/89.

Photograph not
available at press time

Photograph not
available at press time

Model No. 2929
COLLIE - Wall Plaque

Designer:	Unknown	
Height:	Unknown	
Colours:	Golden brown and white - matt	
Issued:	1986-1989	
Series:	Best of Breed	

Description:	U.K. £	U.S. $	Can. $
Matt	45.00	150.00	35.00

Note: Head from model no. 2581 mounted on wood

Model No. 2932
ALSATIAN - Wall Plaque

Designer:	Unknown	
Height:	Unknown	
Colours:	Black and cream - matt	
Issued:	1986-1989	
Series:	Best of Breed	

Description:	U.K. £	U.S. $	Can. $
Matt	45.00	150.00	35.00

Note: Head from model no. 2587 mounted on wood.

Model No. 2946
MEAL TIME

Designer:	Unknown
Height:	3 1/2", 8.9 cm
Colours:	White and tan - gloss
Issued:	1986-1989
Series:	Playful Puppies

Description:	U.K. £	U.S. $	Can. $
Gloss	40.00	50.00	75.00

Note: Taken from Royal Doulton HN 1158.

Model No. 2947
GNAWING

Designer:	Unknown
Height:	4 1/4", 10.8 cm
Colours:	White and tan - gloss
Issued:	1986-1989
Series:	Playful Puppies

Description:	U.K. £	U.S. $	Can. $
Gloss	40.00	50.00	65.00

Note: Taken from Royal Doulton HN 1159.

Model No. 2948
PLAY TIME

Designer:	Unknown
Height:	3 3/4", 9.5 cm
Colours:	White and tan - gloss
Issued:	1986-1989
Series:	Playful Pupies

Description:	U.K. £	U.S. $	Can. $
Gloss	40.00	50.00	65.00

Note: Taken from Royal Doulton HN 2664.

Model No. 2949
JUGGLING

Designer:	Unknown
Height:	3", 7.6 cm
Colours:	White and tan - gloss
Issued:	1986-1989
Series:	Playful Puppies

Description:	U.K. £	U.S. $	Can. $
Gloss	40.00	50.00	65.00

Note: Taken from Royal Doulton HN 1103.

Model No. 2950
NAP TIME

Designer:	Unknown		
Height:	4 1/2", 11.9 cm		
Colours:	White and tan - gloss		
Issued:	1986-1989		
Series:	Playful Puppies		

Description:	*U.K. £*	*U.S. $*	*Can. $*
Gloss	40.00	50.00	65.00

Note: Taken from Royal Doulton HN 1099.

Model No. 2951
CAUGHT IT

Designer:	Unknown		
Height:	2 3/4", 7.0 cm		
Colours:	White and tan - gloss		
Issued:	1986-1989		
Series:	Playful Puppies		

Description:	*U.K. £*	*U.S. $*	*Can. $*
Gloss	40.00	50.00	65.00

Note: Taken from Royal Doulton HN 1097.

Model No. 2980
SPANIEL - on plinth

Designer:	Alan Maslankowski		
Height:	8 1/4", 21.0 cm		
Colours:	Black; Black and white; Golden;		
	Orange and white - matt		
Issued:	1987-1989		
Series:	Spirited Dogs		

Description:	*U.K. £*	*U.S. $*	*Can. $*
Black or white	75.00	150.00	150.00
Black/white	75.00	150.00	150.00
Golden	75.00	150.00	150.00
Orange/white	75.00	150.00	150.00

Model No. 2982
PEKINESE - Begging

Designer:	Alan Maslankowski		
Height:	5 1/2", 14.0 cm		
Colours:	Cream - gloss or matt		
Issued:	1987-1989		
Series:	Good Companions		

Description:	*U.K. £*	*U.S. $*	*Can. $*
1: Gloss	65.00	55.00	75.00
2: Matt	65.00	55.00	75.00

Note: Transferred to R.D. backstamp (DA113) gloss.

Model No. 2984
NORFOLK TERRIER

Designer:	Alan Maslankowski
Height:	4", 10.1 cm
Colours:	Brown - gloss or matt
Issued:	1987-1989
Series:	Good Companions

Description:	U.K. £	U.S. $	Can. $
1: Gloss	40.00	55.00	65.00
2: Matt	40.00	55.00	65.00

Note: Transferred to R.D. backstamp (DA114) gloss.

Model No. 2985
POODLE - on cushion

Designer:	Alan Maslankowski
Height:	5 1/2", 14.0 cm
Colours:	White poodle, turquoise cushion - gloss or matt
Issued:	1987-1989
Series:	Good Companions

Description:	U.K. £	U.S. $	Can. $
1: Gloss	40.00	55.00	65.00
2: Matt	40.00	55.00	65.00

Note: Transferred to R.D. backstamp (DA115) in gloss.

Model No. 2986

SETTER - on ceramic plinth

Designer: Graham Tongue
Height: 8 1/2", 21.6 cm
Series: See below

Colours	Issued	Series	U.K. £	Price U.S. $	Can. $
Black - matt	1987-1989	Spirited Dogs	75.00	150.00	100.00
Black and tan - matt	1988-1989	Spirited Dogs	75.00	150.00	195.00
Bronze	1989-1993	Britannia	65.00	150.00	125.00
Deep red brown	1987-1989	Spirited Dogs	75.00	150.00	195.00
White - matt	1987-1989	Spirited Dogs	75.00	150.00	195.00
White and black	1987-1989	Spirited Dogs	75.00	150.00	195.00

Model No. 3011

POINTER

Designer: Graham Tongue
Height: 8 1/2", 21.6 cm
Series: See below

Colours	Issued	Series	U.K. £	Price U.S. $	Can. $
Black - matt	1987-1989	Spirited Dogs	75.00	150.00	100.00
Bronze finish	1989-1993	Britannia	65.00	150.00	125.00
White - matt	1987-1989	Spirited Dogs	75.00	150.00	100.00
White/brown - matt	1987-1989	Spirited Dogs	75.00	150.00	'195.00

Note: Transferred to R.D. backstamp (DA110) 08/89 - white/brown in matt.

Model No. 3056
ROTTWEILER

Designer:	Alan Maslankowski
Height:	5 1/4", 13.3 cm
Colours:	Black and tan - gloss or matt
Issued:	1: Gloss - 1988-1989
	2: Matt: 1988-1989

Description:	U.K. £	U.S. $	Can. $
1: Gloss	65.00	75.00	125.00
2: Matt	65.00	75.00	125.00

Note: Transferred to R.D. backstamp (DA 99) in gloss.

Model No. 3058
OLD ENGLISH SHEEP DOG - Walking

Designer:	Warren Platt
Height:	5 1/2", 14.0 cm
Colours:	Grey and white - gloss or matt
Issued:	1988-1989

Description:	U.K. £	U.S. $	Can. $
1: Gloss	65.00	75.00	125.00
2: Matt	65.00	75.00	125.00

Note: Transferred to R.D. backstamp (DA100) in gloss.

Model No. 3060
STAFFORDSHIRE BULL TERRIER

Designer:	Alan Maslankowski
Height:	4", 10.1 cm
Colours:	1: White and tan - gloss or matt
	2:. Brindle - gloss or matt
Issued:	1988-1989

Description:	U.K. £	U.S. $	Can. $
1A: White/tan gloss	50.00	75.00	100.00
1B: White/tan matt	50.00	75.00	100.00
2A: Brindle - gloss	50.00	75.00	100.00
2B: Brindle - matt	50.00	75.00	100.00

Note: Transferred to R.D. backstamp (DA101) in gloss.

Model No. 3062A
LABRADOR - on ceramic plinth

Designer:	Alan Maslankowski
Height:	6 1/2", 16.5 cm
Colours:	Black or golden - matt
Issued:	1988-1989
Series:	Spirited Dogs
Varieties:	3062B

Description:	U.K. £	U.S. $	Can. $
1: Black	75.00	150.00	150.00
2: Golden	75.00	150.00	140.00

Note: Transferred to R.D. backstamp (DA111) in golden.

Model No. 3062B
LABRADOR - Standing

Designer:	Alan Maslankowski
Height:	5", 12.7 cm
Colours:	Chocolate brown - gloss
Issued:	1993 in a limited edition of 93
Varieties:	3062A

Description:	U.K. £	U.S. $	Can. $
Chocolate brown	95.00	150.00	175.00

Note: Produced for the B.C.C. with a special BCC Backstamp.

Model No. 3066
RETRIEVER - on ceramic plinth

Designer:	Graham Tongue	
Height:	7 1/2", 19.1 cm	
Colours:	1: Golden - matt	2: Bronze finish
Issued:	1: 1988-1989	2: 1989-1989
Series:	1: Spirited Dogs	2: Britannia

Description:	U.K. £	U.S. $	Can. $
1: Golden	75.00	125.00	150.00
2: Bronze	65.00	100.00	140.00

Note: Transferred to R.D. backstamp (DA112) in golden.

Model No. 3070
AFGHAN HOUND - Running

Designer:	Alan Maslankowski
Height:	5 1/2", 14.0 cm
Colours:	Light brown and cream - gloss or matt
Issued:	1988-1989

Description:	U.K. £	U.S. $	Can. $
1: Gloss	75.00	125.00	150.00
2: Matt	75.00	125.00	150.00

Note: Tranferred to R.D. backstamp (DA102) in gloss.

Model No. 3073
ALSATIAN - Standing

Designer:	Alan Maslankowski
Height:	5 3/4", 14.6 cm
Colours:	Black and light brown - gloss or matt
Issued:	1988-1989

Description:	U.K. £	U.S. $	Can. $
1: Gloss	65.00	100.00	140.00
2: Matt	65.00	100.00	140.00

Note: Transferred to R.D. backstamp (DA103) in gloss.

Model No. 3080
SHETLAND SHEEPDOG - Seated

Designer:	Alan Maslankowski
Height:	5 1/2", 14.0 cm
Colours:	Golden brown and white - gloss or matt
Issued:	1988-1989
Series:	Good Companions

Description:	U.K. £	U.S. $	Can. $
1: Gloss	65.00	100.00	140.00
2: Matt	60.00	95.00	125.00

Note: Transferred to R.D. backstamp (DA117) in gloss

Model No. 3081
BOXER - Standing

Designer:	Alan Maslankowski
Height:	5 1/2", 14.0 cm
Colours:	Golden brown and white - gloss or matt
Issued:	1988-1989

Description:	U.K. £	U.S. $	Can. $
1: Gloss	65.00	100.00	140.00
2: Matt	60.00	95.00	125.00

Note: Transferred to R.D. backstamp (DA104) in gloss.

Model No. 3082
CAIRN TERRIER - Standing

Designer:	Warren Platt
Height:	4 3/4", 12.1 cm
Colours:	Light brown - gloss or matt
Issued:	1988-1989
Series:	Good Companions

Description:	U.K. £	U.S. $	Can. $
1: Gloss	50.00	80.00	110.00
2: Matt	45.00	90.00	100.00

Note: Transferred to R.D. backstamp (DA118) in gloss

Model No. 3083
YORKSHIRE TERRIER - Seated

Designer:	Warren Platt
Height:	5 1/2", 14.0 cm
Colours:	Grey and light brown - gloss and matt
Issued:	1988-1989
Series:	Good Companions

Description:	U.K. £	U.S. $	Can. $
1: Gloss	60.00	95.00	125.00
2: Matt	55.00	85.00	120.00

Note: Transferred to R.D. backstamp (DA119) in gloss.

Model No. 3103
DACHSHUND - Standing

Designer:	Alan Maslankowski
Height:	4 1/4", 10.8 cm
Colours:	1: Black and tan - gloss or matt
	2: Tan - gloss or matt
Issued:	1987-1989, transferred to DA116
Series:	Good Companions

Description:	U.K. £	U.S. $	Can. $
1A: Black - gloss	45.00	70.00	100.00
1B: Black - matt	45.00	70.00	100.00
2B: Tan - gloss	45.00	70.00	100.00
2B: Tan - matt	45.00	70.00	100.00

Model No. 3121
DOBERMAN

Designer:	Alan Maslankowski
Height:	5 1/4", 13.3 cm
Colours:	1: Black and tan - gloss or matt
Issued:	1988-1989

Description:	U.K. £	U.S. $	Can. $
1: Gloss	55.00	85.00	120.00
2: Matt	55.00	85.00	120.00

Note: Transferred to R.D. backstamp (DA105) in gloss.

Model No. 3129
ROUGH COLLIE

Designer:	Warren Platt
Height:	5 1/2", 14.0 cm
Colours:	Golden brown and white - gloss or matt
Issued:	1988-1989

Description:	U.K. £	U.S. $	Can. $
1: Gloss	55.00	85.00	120.00
2: Matt	55.00	85.00	120.00

Note: Transferred to R.D. backstamp (DA106) in gloss.

Model No. 3135
SPRINGER SPANIEL

Designer:	Amanda Hughes-Lubeck
Height:	5", 12.7 cm
Colours:	Dark brown and white - gloss or matt
Issued:	1988-1989

Description:	U.K. £	U.S. $	Can. $
1: Gloss	65.00	100.00	140.00
2: Matt	65.00	100.00	140.00

Note: Transferred to R.D. backstamp (DA107) in gloss.

Model No. 3149
WEST HIGHLAND TERRIER - Seated

Designer:	Martyn C. R. Alcock
Height:	5", 12.7 cm
Colours:	White - gloss or matt
Issued:	1989-1989
Series:	Good Companions

Description:	U.K. £	U.S. $	Can. $
1: Gloss	55.00	85.00	120.00
2: Matt	50.00	80.00	110.00

Note: Transferred to R.D. backstamp (DA120) in gloss.

Model No. 3155
CAVALIER KING CHARLES SPANIEL - Standing

Designer:	Warren Platt
Height:	5 1/2", 14.0 cm
Colours:	1: Black, tan and white - gloss or matt
	2: Tan and white - gloss or matt
Issued:	1989-1989, transferred to DA121 - gloss
Series:	Good Companions

Description:	U.K. £	U.S. $	Can. $
1A: Gloss	60.00	95.00	125.00
1B: Matt	55.00	80.00	120.00
2A: Gloss	60.00	95.00	125.00
2B: Matt	55.00	80.00	120.00

Model No. 3258
ALSATIAN - Standing

Designer:	Unknown
Height:	4 1/4", 10.8 cm
Colours:	Black and cream - gloss
Issued:	1991 to the present

Description:	U.K. £	U.S. $	Can. $
Gloss	11.50	N/A	N/A

Model No. 3260
ROTTWEILER - Standing

Designer:	Unknown
Height:	3 1/2", 8.9 cm
Colours:	Black and tan - gloss
Issued:	1991 to the present

Description:	U.K. £	U.S. $	Can. $
Gloss	11.50	N/A	N/A

Model No. 3262
YORKSHIRE TERRIER - Standing

Designer:	Unknown
Height:	3 1/2", 8.9 cm
Colours:	Grey and sandy brown - gloss
Issued:	1991 to the present

Description:	U.K. £	U.S. $	Can. $
Gloss	9.95	N/A	N/A

Model No. 3270
GOLDEN RETRIEVER - Standing

Designer:	Unknown
Height:	2 3/4", 7.0 cm
Colours:	Pale golden brown - gloss
Issued:	1991 to the present

Description:	U.K. £	U.S. $	Can. $
Gloss	9.95	N/A	N/A

Model No. 3375
HOUNDS - Seated

Designer:	Martyn C. R. Alcock
Height:	2 1/4", 5.7 cm
Colours:	Black, tan and white - gloss
Issued:	1993 to the present

Description:	U.K. £	U.S. $	Can. $
Gloss	11.50	33.00	35.00

Model No. 3376
GOLDEN RETRIEVERS - Seated

Designer:	Martyn C. R. Alcock
Height:	2", 5.0 cm
Colours:	Golden brown - gloss
Issued:	1993 to the present

Description:	U.K. £	U.S. $	Can. $
Gloss	11.50	33.00	35.00

Model No. 3377
COCKER SPANIEL - Standing

Designer:	Amanda Hughes-Lubeck
Height:	3", 7.6 cm
Colours:	Golden brown - gloss
Issued:	1993 to the present

Description:	U.K. £	U.S. $	Can. $
Gloss	9.95	33.00	35.00

Model No. 3378
ALSATIAN - Lying

Designer:	Amanda Hughes-Lubeck
Height:	2 1/2", 6.4 cm
Colours:	Black and cream - gloss
Issued:	1993 to the present

Description:	U.K. £	U.S. $	Can. $
Gloss	9.95	33.00	45.00

Model No. 3379
BULLDOG - Seated

Designer:	Warren Platt
Height:	2 1/2", 6.4 cm
Colours:	White with pale tan patch - gloss
Issued:	1993 to the present

Description:	U.K. £	U.S. $	Can. $
Gloss	9.95	33.00	35.00

Model No. 3380
JACK RUSSELL TERRIER - Standing

Designer:	Warren Platt
Height:	2 1/2", 6.4 cm
Colours:	White with pale brown ears and patches on head - gloss
Issued:	1993 to the present

Description:	U.K. £	U.S. $	Can. $
Gloss	9.95	33.00	35.00

Model No. 3381
RETRIEVER - Standing

Designer:	Warren Platt
Height:	2", 5.0 cm
Colours:	Golden brown - gloss
Issued:	1993 to the present

Description:	U.K. £	U.S. $	Can. $
Gloss	9.95	33.00	35.00

Model No. 3382
SCOTTISH TERRIER - Standing

Designer:	Martyn C. R. Alcock
Height:	3", 7.6 cm
Colours:	Black - gloss
Issued:	1993 to the present

Description:	U.K. £	U.S. $	Can. $
Gloss	9.95	33.00	35.00

Model No. 3383
COCKER SPANIELS - Seated

Designer:	Martyn C. R. Alcock
Height:	2", 5.0 cm
Colours:	Golden brown - gloss
Issued:	1993 to the present

Description:	U.K. £	U.S. $	Can. $
Gloss	11.50	33.00	35.00

Model No. 3384
BULLDOGS - Seated

Designer:	Martyn C. R. Alcock
Height:	2 1/4", 5.7 cm
Colours:	White with pale tan patches - gloss
Issued:	1994 to the present

Description:	U.K. £	U.S. $	Can. $
Gloss	9.95	18.00	35.00

Model No. 3385
DALMATIAN - Standing

Designer:	Amanda Hughes-Lubeck
Height:	3", 7.6 cm
Colours:	White with black spots - gloss
Issued:	1994 to the present

Description:	U.K. £	U.S. $	Can. $
Gloss	9.95	18.00	35.00

Model No. 3436
CAVALIER KING CHARLES SPANIEL - Seated

Designer:	Amanda Hughes-Lubeck
Height:	2 1/2", 6.4 cm
Colours:	White with golden brown patches - gloss
Issued:	1994 to the present

Description:	U.K. £	U.S. $	Can. $
Gloss	9.95	18.00	35.00

Photograph not
available at press time

Model No. 3467
WEST HIGHLAND WHITE TERRIERS - Seated

Designer:	Amanda Hughes-Lubeck
Height:	2", 5.0 cm
Colours:	White - gloss
Issued:	1994 to the present

Description:	U.K. £	U.S. $	Can. $
Gloss	9.95	18.00	35.00

Model No. 3468
OLD ENGLISH SHEEPDOGS - Seated

Designer:	Warren Platt
Height:	2", 5.0 cm
Colours:	Grey and white - gloss
Issued:	1995 to the present

Description:	U.K. £	U.S. $	Can. $
Gloss	10.95	19.00	50.00

Model No. 3475
BOXERS - One seated, one lying

Designer: Amanda Hughes-Lubeck
Height: 2 1/4", 5.7 cm
Colours: Tan - gloss
Issued: 1995 to the present

Description:	U.K. £	U.S. $	Can. $
Gloss	12.95	19.00	45.00

Photograph not
available at press time

Model No. 3490
ROTTWEILERS - One seated, one lying

Designer: Warren Platt
Height: 2", 5.0 cm
Colours: Black and tan - gloss
Issued: 1995 to the present

Description:	U.K. £	U.S. $	Can. $
Gloss	12.95	19.00	50.00

Chapter Five

FARM ANIMALS - CATTLE

As the number of Beswick collectors grows dramatically, this particular section of Beswick animals has become more popular. This is mainly due to the accurate reproduction of champion-stock animals, where meticulous attention to detail by the designers and modellers at the Beswick factory, and now the Beswick Studio of Royal Doulton, has produced some superb models over the years.

This is very noticeable with the Hereford Cattle, since as the breed standard has changed, the models have been updated. Just compare the models of the early Herefords with the ones that followed; they are very different in shape.

It is also interesting to note that when the calves were discontinued in the mid 1970s, with the exception of the Friesian, public pressure brought about their reintroduction ten years later. Although the later models were altered from the originals, they can all live together as one happy family. Thus, for example, *Aberdeen Angus Cattle* becomes a set of four rather than just three.

The models of the best-known breeds have survived to the present, but the lesser-known breeds, such as the Galloways, sadly had a short production run and now, as a result, are highly sought after by collectors.

The *Connoisseur Range* of cattle on polished wooden bases is truly impressive. With a satin matt finish, more detail can generally be achieved than on the gloss models—this, of course, was reflected in the retail price.

Many models are still in production, after nearly forty years in some cases, and surely this indicates how popular they have been and still are today.

MODEL NUMBER INDEX

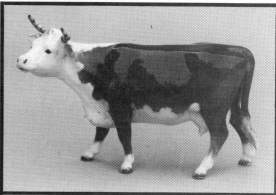

Model No. 854
HEREFORD CALF

Designer:	Arthur Gredington
Height:	4 1/2", 11.9 cm
Colour:	1: Brown and white - gloss
	2: Roan - gloss
	3: Blue
Issued:	1940-c.1957

Description:	U.K. £	U.S. $	Can. $
1: Brown / white	75.00	100.00	150.00
2: Roan	100.00	150.00	250.00
3: Blue	100.00	150.00	250.00

Model No. 899
HEREFORD COW
Version One - Horns are upright

Designer:	Arthur Gredington
Height:	5", 12.7 cm
Colour:	Brown and white - gloss
Issued:	1941-1941
Varieties:	948 (Horns point forward)

Description:	U.K. £	U.S. $	Can. $
Gloss	185.00	300.00	450.00

Note: Model no. 899 was remodelled in 1941 and became model no. 948.

Model No. 901A
HEREFORD CALF
Version One - Mouth open

Designer:	Arthur Gredington
Height:	4", 10.1 cm
Colour:	Roan and white - gloss
Issued:	1940-Unknown
Varieties:	901B (mouth closed)

Description:	U.K. £	U.S. $	Can. $
Gloss	150.00	250.00	325.00

Model No. 901B
HEREFORD CALF
Version Two - Mouth closed

Designer:	Arthur Gredington
Height:	3 3/4", 9.5 cm
Colour:	Brown and white - gloss
Issued:	Unknown-c.1957
Varieties:	901A (mouth open)

Description:	U.K. £	U.S. $	Can. $
Gloss	75.00	100.00	175.00

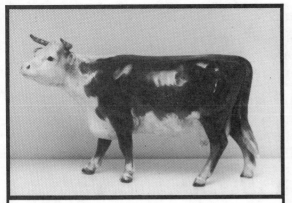

Model No. 948
HEREFORD COW
Version Two - Horns point forward

Designer:	Arthur Gredington		
Height:	5", 12.7 cm		
Colour:	Brown and white - gloss		
Issued:	1941-c.1957		
Varieties:	899 (horns are upright)		

Description:	U.K. £	U.S. $	Can. $
Gloss	115.00	200.00	275.00

Note: Model no. 948 was remodelled in 1941 from model no. 899.

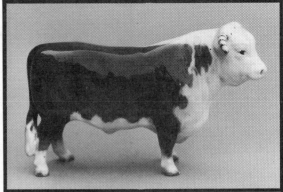

Model No. 949
HEREFORD BULL

Designer:	Arthur Gredington
Height:	5 3/4", 14.6 cm
Colour:	Brown and white - gloss
Issued:	1941-c.1957

Description:	U.K. £	U.S. $	Can. $
Gloss	150.00	250.00	350.00

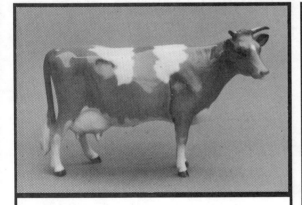

Model No. 1248A
GUERNSEY COW
Version One - Horns and ears separate

Designer:	Arthur Gredington
Height:	4 1/4", 10.8 cm
Colour:	Tan, brown and white - gloss
Issued:	1952-1953
Varieties:	1248B (Horns and ears moulded together)

Description:	U.K. £	U.S. $	Can. $
Gloss	125.00	225.00	325.00

Note: Modelled from the Standard of the Guernsey Cattle Society.

Model No. 1248B
GUERNSEY COW
Version Two - Horns and ears are moulded together

Designer:	Arthur Gredington
Height:	4 1/4", 10.8 cm
Colour:	Tan/brown and white - gloss or matt
Issued:	1: Gloss - 1953-1989
	2: Matt - 1985-1989
Varieties:	1248A (Horns and ears separate)

Description:	U.K. £	U.S. $	Can. $
1: Gloss	85.00	125.00	200.00
2: Matt	75.00	125.00	175.00

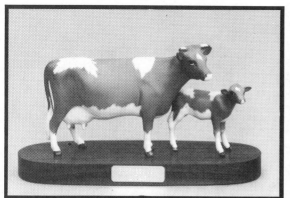

Model No. 1248B/1249A
GUERNSEY COW AND CALF - on wooden plinth

Designer:	Arthur Gredington
Height:	4 1/4", 10.8 cm
Colour:	Tan/brown and white - matt
Issued:	c.1988

Description:	U.K. £	U.S. $	Can. $
Matt	110.00	200.00	325.00

Note: Cow is no. 1248B; Calf is no. 1249A. Issued as a special commission for the Guernsey Cattle Society c.1988

Model No. 1249A
GUERNSEY CALF

Designer:	Arthur Gredington
Height:	2 3/4", 7.0 cm
Colour:	Tan-brown and white - gloss or matt
Issued:	1: Gloss - 1952-1975
	2: Matt - 1987-1989
Re-issued:	1: Gloss - 1985-1989

Description:	U.K. £	U.S. $	Can. $
1: Gloss	45.00	85.00	125.00
1: Gloss Re-issued	35.00	70.00	100.00
2: Matt	35.00	70.00	100.00

Model No. 1249B
AYRSHIRE CALF

Designer:	Arthur Gredington
Height:	2 3/4", 7.0 cm
Colour:	Brown and white - gloss or matt
Modelled:	1952
Issued:	1: Gloss - 1956-1975
	2: Matt - 1987-1989
Re:issued:	1: Gloss - 1985-1990

Description:	U.K. £	U.S. $	Can. $
1: Gloss	45.00	85.00	125.00
1: Gloss Re-issued	35.00	70.00	100.00
2: Matt	35.00	70.00	100.00

Model No. 1249C
FRIESIAN CALF

Designer:	Arthur Gredington
Height:	2 3/4", 7.0 cm
Colour:	Black and white - gloss or matt
Modelled:	1952
Issued:	1: Gloss - 1956 to the present
	2: Matt - 1987-1989

Description:	U.K. £	U.S. $	Can. $
1: Gloss	12.95	N/A	N/A
2: Matt	30.00	45.00	65.00

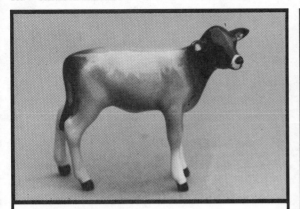

Model No. 1249D
JERSEY CALF

Designer:	Arthur Gredington
Height:	2 3/4", 6.4 cm
Colour:	Light brown with shading darker around the head - gloss or matt
Issued:	1: 1956-1975
	2: 1987-1989
Reissued:	1: 1985 to the present

Description:	U.K. £	U.S. $	Can. $
1: Gloss	45.00	85.00	125.00
1: Gloss Reissued	12.95	N/A	N/A
2 Matt	35.00	70.00	100.00

Model No. 1249E
HEREFORD CALF

Designer:	Arthur Gredington
Height:	2 3/4", 7.0 cm
Colour:	Brown and white - gloss
Modelled:	1952
Issued:	This model was especially commissioned, sometime between 1975 and 1985, when the only calf in production was the Friesian.

Description:	U.K. £	U.S. $	Can. $
Gloss	60.00	100.00	125.00

Model No. 1345
JERSEY COW CH. "NEWTON TINKLE"

Designer:	Arthur Gredington
Height:	4 1/4", 10.8 cm
Colour:	Light brown with shading darker around the head - gloss or matt
Issued:	1: Gloss - 1954 to the present
	2: Matt - 1985-1989

Description:	U.K. £	U.S. $	Can. $
1: Gloss	27.95	N/A	N/A
2: Matt	55.00	85.00	125.00

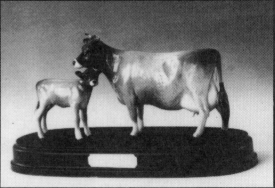

Model No. 1345/1249D
JERSEY COW AND CALF

Designer:	Arthur Gredington
Height:	5 1/4", 13.3 cm
Colour:	Light brown with shading especially around the head - gloss
Issued:	1993 to the present
Series:	Plinthed Animals

Description:	U.K. £	U.S. $	Can. $
Gloss	47.00	N/A	N/A

Note: Cow is no. 1345; Calf is no. 1249D.

Model No. 1350
AYRSHIRE COW CH. "ICKHAM BESSIE"

Designer: Arthur Gredington
Height: 5", 12.7 cm
Colour: Brown and white - gloss or matt
Issued: 1: Gloss - 1954-1990
            2: Matt - 1985-1989

Description:	U.K. £	U.S. $	Can. $
1: Gloss	75.00	125.00	175.00
2: Matt	75.00	125.00	175.00

Model No. 1360
HEREFORD COW

Designer: Arthur Gredington
Height: 4 1/4", 10.8 cm
Colour: Brown and white - gloss or matt
Issued: 1: Gloss - 1954 to the present
            2: Matt - 1985-1989

Description:	U.K. £	U.S. $	Can. $
1: Gloss	27.95	N/A	N/A
2: Matt	55.00	85.00	125.00

Note: Modelled from the standard of the Hereford Cattle Society.

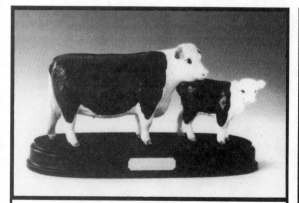

Model No. 1360/1827C
HEREFORD COW AND CALF - on wooden plinth

Designer: Graham Tongue
Height: 7", 17.8 cm
Colour: Brown and white - gloss
Issued: 1993 to the present
Series: Plinthed Animals

Description:	U.K. £	U.S. $	Can. $
Gloss	47.00	N/A	N/A

Note: Cow is no. 1360; Calf is no. 1827C.

Model No. 1362A
FRIESIAN COW
CH. "CLAYBURY LEEGWATER"

Designer: Arthur Gredington
Height: 4 1/2", 11.9 cm
Colour: Black and white - gloss or matt
Issued: 1: Gloss - 1954 to the present
            2: Matt - 1985-1989
Varieties: 1362B

Description:	U.K. £	U.S. $	Can. $
1: Gloss	27.95	N/A	N/A
2: Matt	55.00	85.00	125.00

Model No. 1362B
RED FRIESIAN COW

Designer:	Arthur Gredington
Height:	4 1/2", 11.9 cm
Colour:	Brown and white - gloss
Modelled:	1954
Issued:	1992 in an edition of 130
Varieties:	1362A

Description:	U.K. £	U.S. $	Can. $
Gloss	200.00	325.00	450.00

Note: Produced for the Beswick Collectors Circle with special B.C.C. and Beswick backstamps.

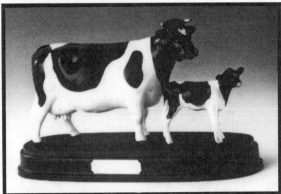

Model No. 1362/1249C
FRIESIAN COW AND CALF - on wooden plinth

Designer:	Graham Tongue
Height:	5 1/2", 14.0 cm
Colour:	Black and white - gloss
Issued:	1993 to the present
Series:	Plinthed Animals

Description:	U.K. £	U.S. $	Can. $
Gloss	47.00	N/A	N/A

Note: Cow is no. 1362; Calf is no. 1249C.

Model No. 1363
HEREFORD BULL

Designer:	Arthur Gredington
Height:	4 1/2", 10.8 cm
Colour:	Brown and white - gloss or matt
Issued:	1: Gloss - 1955 to the present
	2: Matt - 1985-1989

Description:	U.K. £	U.S. $	Can. $
1: Gloss	27.95	N/A	N/A
2: Matt	55.00	85.00	125.00

Note: Modelled from the standard of the Hereford Cattle Society.
Note: This model has also appeared as a money-box.

Model No. A1363
HEREFORD BULL - on wooden plinth

Designer:	Arthur Gredington
Height:	5 1/2", 14.0 cm
Colour:	Brown and white - satin matt
Modelled:	1955
Issued:	1968-1975
Series:	Connoisseur

Description:	U.K. £	U.S. $	Can. $
Satin matt	150.00	250.00	350.00

Note: Issued on a teak stand. The base was changed to polished wood in 1974.

Model No. 1406A
ABERDEEN ANGUS CALF

Designer:	Arthur Gredington		
Height:	3", 7.6 cm		
Colour:	Black - gloss		
Issued:	1956-1975		

Description:	U.K. £	U.S. $	Can. $
Gloss	55.00	85.00	125.00

Model No. 1406B
HEREFORD CALF

Designer:	Arthur Gredington		
Height:	3", 7.6 cm		
Colour:	Brown and white - gloss		
Issued:	1956-1975		

Description:	U.K. £	U.S. $	Can. $
Gloss	85.00	150.00	200.00

Model No. 1406C
DAIRY SHORTHORN CALF

Designer:	Arthur Gredington		
Height:	3", 7.6 cm		
Colour:	Brown and white with shading - gloss		
Issued:	1956-1973		

Description:	U.K. £	U.S. $	Can. $
Gloss	150.00	250.00	350.00

Model No. 1422
JERSEY BULL CH. "DUNSLEY COY BOY"

Designer:	Arthur Gredington	
Height:	4 1/2", 11.9 cm	
Colour:	Light brown with shading and darker head - gloss or matt	
Issued	1: Gloss - 1956 to the present	
	2: Matt - 1985-1989	

Description:	U.K. £	U.S. $	Can. $
1: Gloss	27.95	N/A	N/A
2: Matt	45.00	75.00	100.00

Model No. 1439A
FRIESIAN BULL
CH. "CODDINGTON HILT BAR"

Designer:	Arthur Gredington		
Height:	4 3/4", 12.1 cm		
Colour:	Black and white - gloss or matt		
Issued:	1: Gloss - 1956 to the present		
	2: Matt - 1985-1989		

Description:	U.K. £	U.S. $	Can. $
1: Gloss	33.00	N/A	N/A
2: Matt	55.00	85.00	125.00

Model No. 1439B
FRIESIAN BULL - on teak plinth

Designer:	Arthur Gredington
Height:	5 1/2", 14.0 cm
Colour:	Black and white - Satin matt
Modelled:	1956
Issued:	1968-1973
Varieties:	1439A
Series:	Connoisseur Cattle

Description:	U.K. £	U.S. $	Can. $
Satin matt	150.00	250.00	350.00

Model No. 1439C
RED FRIESIAN BULL

Designer:	Arthur Gredington
Height:	4 3/4", 12.1 cm
Colour:	Brown and white - gloss
Modelled:	1956
Issued:	1992 in an edition of 129

Description:	U.K. £	U.S. $	Can. $
Gloss	200.00	350.00	450.00

Note: Produced for the Beswick Collectors Circle with special B.C.C. and Beswick backstamps.

Model No. 1451
GUERNSEY BULL
CH. "SABRINA'S SIR RICHMOND 14TH"

Designer:	Colin Melbourne
Height:	4 3/4", 11.9 cm
Colour:	Tan/brown and white - gloss or matt
Issued:	1: Gloss - 1956-1989
	2: Matt - 1985-1989

Description:	U.K. £	U.S. $	Can. $
1: Gloss	75.00	125.00	175.00
2: Matt	85.00	125.00	175.00

Photograph not
available at press time

Model No. 1454A
AYRSHIRE BULL CH. "WHITEHILL MANDATE"
Version One

Designer:	Colin Melbourne	
Height:	5 1/4", 13.3 cm	
Colour:	Brown and white with shading - gloss	
Issued:	1956-1957	

Description:	U.K. £	U.S. $	Can. $
Gloss		Rare	

Model No. 1454B
AYRSHIRE BULL CH. "WHITEHILL MANDATE"
Version Two

Designer:	Colin Melbourne	
Height:	5 1/4", 13.3 cm	
Colour:	Brown, white and shaded - gloss or matt	
Issued:	1: Gloss - 1957-1990	
	2: Matt - 1985-1989	

Description:	U.K. £	U.S. $	Can. $
1: Gloss	85.00	125.00	175.00
2: Matt	75.00	125.00	175.00

Model No. 1504
DAIRY SHORTHORN BULL
CH. "GWERSYLT LORD OXFORD 74TH"

Designer:	Arthur Gredington	
Height:	5", 12.7 cm	
Colour:	Brown and white with shading - gloss	
Issued:	1957-1973	

Description:	U.K. £	U.S. $	Can. $
Gloss	275.00	450.00	600.00

Model No. 1510
DAIRY SHORTHORN COW
CH. "EATON WILD EYES 91ST"

Designer:	Arthur Gredington	
Height:	4 3/4", 12.1 cm	
Colour:	Brown and white with shading - gloss	
Issued:	1957-1973	

Description:	U.K. £	U.S. $	Can. $
Gloss	275.00	450.00	600.00

Model No. 1562
ABERDEEN ANGUS BULL

Designer: Arthur Gredington
Height: 4 1/2", 11.9 cm
Colour: Black - gloss or matt
Issued: 1: Gloss - 1958-1989
  2: Matt - 1985-1989

Description:	U.K. £	U.S. $	Can. $
1: Gloss	75.00	125.00	175.00
2: Matt	75.00	125.00	175.00

Note: This model was approved by a panel of judges of the Breed Society.

Model No. 1563
ABERDEEN ANGUS COW

Designer: Arthur Gredington
Height: 4 1/4", 10.8 cm
Colour: Black - gloss or matt
Issued: 1: Gloss - 1959-1989
  2: Matt - 1985-1989

Description:	U.K. £	U.S. $	Can. $
1: Gloss	75.00	125.00	175.00
2: Matt	75.00	125.00	175.00

Note: This model was approved by a panel of judges of the Breed Society.

Model No. 1740
HIGHLAND COW

Designer: Arthur Gredington
Height: 5 1/4", 3.3 cm
Colour: Tan and brown - gloss or matt
Issued: 1: Gloss - 1961-1990
  2: Matt - 1985-1989

Description:	U.K. £	U.S. $	Can. $
1: Gloss	75.00	125.00	175.00
2: Matt	75.00	125.00	175.00

Photograph not
available at press time

Model No. 1746A
GALLOWAY BULL

Designer: Arthur Gredington
Height: 4 1/2", 11.9 cm
Colour: Black - gloss
Modelled: 1961
Issued: 1962-1969
Varieties: 1746B, 1746C

Description:	U.K. £	U.S. $	Can. $
Gloss	300.00	475.00	650.00

Model No. 1746B
GALLOWAY BULL - BELTED

Designer:	Arthur Gredington
Height:	4 1/2", 11.9 cm
Colour:	Black and white - gloss
Modelled:	1961
Issued:	1963-1969
Varieties:	1746A, 1746C

Description:	*U.K. £*	*U.S. $*	*Can. $*
Gloss	400.00	650.00	900.00

Model No. 1746C
GALLOWAY BULL - SILVER DUNN

Designer:	Arthur Gredington
Height:	4 1/2", 11.9 cm
Colour:	Fawn and brown - gloss
Modelled:	1961
Issued:	1962-1969
Varieties:	1746A, 1746B

Description:	*U.K. £*	*U.S. $*	*Can. $*
Gloss	300.00	475.00	650.00

Model No. 1827A
ABERDEEN ANGUS CALF

Designer:	Arthur Gredington
Height:	3", 7.6 cm
Colour:	Black - gloss or matt
Issued:	1: Gloss - 1985-1989
	2: Matt - 1987-1989

Description:	*U.K. £*	*U.S. $*	*Can. $*
1: Gloss	35.00	55.00	75.00
2: Matt	35.00	55.00	75.00

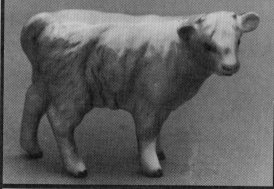

Model No. 1827B
CHAROLAIS CALF

Designer:	Arthur Gredington
Height:	3", 7.6 cm
Colour:	Cream - gloss or matt
Issued:	1: Gloss - 1985 to the present
	2: Matt - 1987-1989

Description:	*U.K. £*	*U.S. $*	*Can. $*
1: Gloss	12.95	N/A	N/A
2: Matt	25.00	40.00	60.00

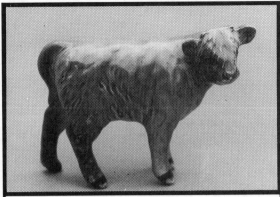

Model No. 1827C
HEREFORD CALF

Designer: Arthur Gredington
Height: 3", 7.6 cm
Colour: Brown and white - gloss or matt
Issued: 1: Gloss - 1985 to the present
              2: Matt - 1987-1989

Description:	U.K. £	U.S. $	Can. $
1: Gloss	12.95	N/A	N/A
2: Matt	35.00	55.00	75.00

Model No. 1827D
HIGHLAND CALF

Designer: Arthur Gredington
Height: 3", 7.6 cm
Colour: Tan/brown - gloss or matt
Issued: 1: Gloss - 1962-1990
              2: Matt - 1987-1989

Description:	U.K. £	U.S. $	Can. $
1: Gloss	35.00	N/A	N/A
2: Matt	35.00	55.00	75.00

Model No. 2008
HIGHLAND BULL

Designer: Arthur Gredington
Height: 5", 12.7 cm
Colour: Tan/brown - gloss or matt
Issued: 1: Gloss - 1965-1990
              2: Matt - 1985-1989

Description:	U.K. £	U.S. $	Can. $
1: Gloss	75.00	125.00	175.00
2: Matt	75.00	125.00	175.00

Model No. 2463
CHAROLAIS BULL

Designer: Alan Maslankowski
Height: 5", 12.7 cm
Colour: Cream - gloss or matt
Modelled: 1973
Issued: 1: Gloss - 1979 to the present
              2: Matt - 1985-1989

Description:	U.K. £	U.S. $	Can. $
1: Gloss	33.00	N/A	N/A
2: Matt	45.00	75.00	100.00

Model No. A2463
CHAROLAIS BULL - on wooden plinth

Designer:	Alan Maslankowski		
Height:	5 1/2", 14.0 cm		
Colour:	Cream - satin matt		
Modelled:	1973		
Issued:	1975-1979		
Series:	Connoisseur Cattle		

Description:	*U.K. £*	*U.S. $*	*Can. $*
Satin matt	150.00	200.00	350.00

Model No. A2542
HEREFORD BULL - on wooden plinth

Designer:	Graham Tongue		
Height:	7 1/2", 19.1 cm		
Colour:	Brown and white - satin matt		
Modelled:	1975		
Issued:	1976-1989		
Series:	Connoisseur Cattle		

Description:	*U.K. £*	*U.S. $*	*Can. $*
Gloss	120.00	200.00	250.00

Note: Transferred to R.D.backstamp, DA19, 08/89.

Model No. 2549
POLLED HEREFORD BULL

Designer:	Graham Tongue		
Height:	5", 12.7 cm		
Colour:	Brown and white, ring through nose - gloss or matt		
Modelled:	1975		
Issued:	1: Gloss - 1977 to the present 2: Matt - 1985-1989		

Description:	*U.K. £*	*U.S. $*	*Can. $*
1: Gloss	55.00	N/A	N/A
2: Matt	60.00	95.00	135.00

Model No. A2574
POLLED HEREFORD BULL - on wooden plinth

Designer:	Graham Tongue		
Height:	7 1/2", 19.1 cm		
Colour:	Brown and white - satin matt		
Modelled:	1976		
Issued:	1977-1989		
Series:	Connoisseur Cattle		

Description:	*U.K. £*	*U.S. $*	*Can. $*
Satin matt	120.00	200.00	250.00

Note: Transferred to R.D.backstamp, DA21, 08/89.

Model No. A2580
FRIESIAN BULL - on wooden plinth

Designer:	Graham Tongue
Height:	7 1/2", 19.1 cm
Colour:	Black and white - satin matt
Modelled:	1976
Issued:	1978-1989
Series:	Connoisseur Cattle

Description:	*U.K. £*	*U.S. $*	*Can. $*
Satin matt	120.00	200.00	250.00

Note: Transferred to R.D. backstamp (DA23), 08/89.

Model No. A2600
CHAROLAIS BULL - on wooden plinth

Designer:	Graham Tongue
Height:	7 1/2", 19.1 cm
Colour:	Cream - satin matt
Issued:	1971-1979
Series:	Connoisseur Cattle

Description:	*U.K. £*	*U.S. $*	*Can. $*
Satin matt	120.00	200.00	250.00

Note: Transferred R.D. to backstamp (DA27), 08/89.

Model No. A2607
FRIESIAN COW - on wooden plinth

Designer:	Graham Tongue
Height:	7 1/2", 19.1 cm
Colour:	Black and white - satin matt
Modelled:	1977
Issued:	1979-1989
Series:	Connoisseur Cattle

Description:	*U.K. £*	*U.S. $*	*Can. $*
Satin matt	120.00	200.00	250.00

Note: Transferred to R.D. backstamp (DA29), 08/89.

Model No. A2607/2690
FRIESIAN COW AND CALF - on wooden plinth

Designer:	Graham Tongue
Height:	6 1/2", 16.5 cm
Colour:	Black and white - satin matt
Modelled:	Cow - 1977; Calf - 1982
Issued:	1982-1989
Series:	Connoisseur Cattle

Description:	*U.K. £*	*U.S. $*	*Can. $*
Satin matt	150.00	250.00	325.00

Note: Cow is no. A2607; Calf is no. 2690, never issued individually. Transferred to R.D. backstamp (DA3) 08/89.

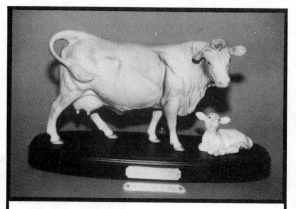

Model No. A2648/2652
CHAROLAIS COW AND CALF - on wooden plinth

Designer:	Graham Tongue
Height:	7 1/4", 18.4 cm
Colour:	Cream - satin matt
Modelled:	1979
Issued:	1981-1989
Series:	Connoissuer

Description:	U.K. £	U.S. $	Can. $
Satin matt	150.00	250.00	325.00

Note: Cow is no. A2648; Calf is no 2652 which was never issued individually. Transferred to R.D. backstamp (DA33), 08/89.

Model No. A2667/2669
HEREFORD COW AND CALF - on wooden plinth

Designer:	Graham Tongue
Height:	7", 17.8 cm
Colour:	Brown and white - satin matt
Modelled:	1980
Issued:	1981-1989
Series:	Connoisseur

Description:	U.K. £	U.S. $	Can. $
Satin matt	150.00	250.00	325.00

Note: Cow is no. A2667; Calf is no 2669, which was never issued individually. Transferred to R.D. backstamp (DA34), 08/89.

Model No. 2690
RED FRIESIAN CALF

Designer:	Graham Tongue
Height:	2 1/4", 5.7 cm
Colour:	Brown and white - gloss
Modelled:	1980
Issued:	1992 in a special edition of 132

Description:	U.K. £	U.S. $	Can. $
Gloss	150.00	250.00	350.00

Note: Produced as a free standing model, in this special colourway for The Beswick Collectors Circle. The B.C.C. backstamp appears in addition to the normal Beswick Backstamp.

Model No. 2792
DAISY THE COW - Creamer

Designer:	Graham Tongue
Height:	5 3/4", 14.6 cm
Colour:	A variety of floral decorations, blue flowers or yellow being the most common, but all on a white background
Issued:	1982-1989
Series:	Fun Ceramics

Description:	U.K. £	U.S. $	Can. $
Blue	65.00	125.00	150.00
Yellow	65.00	125.00	150.00

Model No. 3075
CHAROLAIS COW

Designer:	Unknown
Height:	5", 12.7 cm
Colour:	Cream - gloss or matt
Modelled:	1987
Issued:	1: Gloss - 1988 to the present
	2: Matt - 1988-1989

Description:	*U.K. £*	*U.S. $*	*Can. $*
1: Gloss	27.95	N/A	N/A
2: Matt	75.00	125.00	175.00

Model No. 3075/1827B
CHAROLAIS COW AND CALF - on wooden plinth

Designer:	Unknown
Height:	6", 15.0 cm
Colour:	Cream - gloss
Issued:	1993 to the present

Description:	*U.K. £*	*U.S. $*	*Can. $*
Gloss	47.00	N/A	N/A

Note: Cow is no. 3075; Calf is no. 1827B.

(Illustration courtesy of Royal Doulton.)

FARM ANIMALS

OTHERS

It is surprising that this section was never expanded to include rare breeds, but it does include most of the animals one expects to find on a farm, besides cattle.

With the exception of the earlier models, the majority of the animals in this group are realistically portrayed. Examples of this are the goat and kid, which make a delightful pair, and the donkeys, as popular now as they ever were.

INDEX BY MODEL NUMBER

Photograph not
available at press time

Model No. 323
LAMB ON BASE

Designer: Miss Greaves
Height: 7 1/2", 19.1 cm
Colour: 1: Cream - satin matt
              2: Blue - gloss
Issued: c.1935-By 1954

Description:	U.K. £	U.S. $	Can. $
1: Cream - satin	125.00	200.00	275.00
2: Blue - gloss	175.00	275.00	400.00

Note: This piece was modelled by Miss Greaves in a
       Deco style.

Model No. 369
MULE

Designer: Miss Greaves
Height: 8", 20.3 cm
Colour: 1: Cream - satin matt
              2: Blue - gloss
Issued: 1936-By 1954

Description:	U.K. £	U.S. $	Can. $
1: Cream - satin	125.00	200.00	275.00
2: Blue - gloss	175.00	275.00	400.00

Note: This piece was modelled by Miss Greaves in a
       Deco style.

Model No. 398
GOAT

Designer: Mr. Owen
Height: 4 1/2", 11.9 cm
Colour: 1: Various - satin matt
              2: Blue - gloss
Issued: 1936-By 1954

Description:	U.K. £	U.S. $	Can. $
1: Various - satin	100.00	150.00	225.00
2: Blue - gloss	110.00	175.00	250.00

Model No. 832
PIG

Designer: Arthur Gredington
Height: 3 3/4", 9.5 cm
Colour: White and pink with grey patches - gloss
Issued: 1940-1971
Set: 833, 834

Description:	U.K. £	U.S. $	Can. $
Gloss	75.00	125.00	150.00

Model No. 833
PIGLET - Running

Designer:	Arthur Gredington
Height:	1 3/4", 4.5 cm
Colour:	White and pink with grey patches - gloss
Issued:	1940-1971
Set:	832, 834

Description:	U.K. £	U.S. $	Can. $
Gloss	45.00	75.00	100.00

Model No. 834
PIGLET - Trotting

Designer:	Arthur Gredington
Height:	1 1/2", 3.8 cm
Colour:	White and pink with grey patches - gloss
Issued:	1940-1971
Set:	832, 833

Description:	U.K. £	U.S. $	Can. $
Gloss	45.00	75.00	100.00

Photograph not
available at press time

Model No. 897
DONKEY FOAL

Designer:	Arthur Gredington
Height:	Unknown
Colour:	Natural - gloss
Issued:	1941-Unknown

Description:	U.K. £	U.S. $	Can. $

Probably not put into production under this
number, see no. 950.

Model No. 935
SHEEP

Designer:	Arthur Gredington
Height:	3 1/2", 8.9 cm
Colour:	White - gloss
Issued:	1941-1971
Set:	936, 937, 938

Description:	U.K. £	U.S. $	Can. $
Gloss	45.00	75.00	100.00

Model No. 936
LAMB

Designer: Arthur Gredington
Height: 3 1/4", 8.3 cm
Colour: White - gloss
Issued: 1941-1971
Set: 935, 937, 938

Description:	U.K. £	U.S. $	Can. $
Gloss	35.00	60.00	75.00

Model No. 937
LAMB

Designer: Arthur Gredington
Height: 2", 5.0 cm
Colour: White - gloss
Issued: 1941-1971
Set: 935, 936, 938

Description:	U.K. £	U.S. $	Can. $
Gloss	35.00	60.00	75.00

Model No. 938
LAMB

Designer: Arthur Gredington
Height: 2", 5.0 cm
Colour: White - gloss
Issued: 1941-1971
Set: 935, 936, 937

Description:	U.K. £	U.S. $	Can. $
Gloss	35.00	60.00	75.00

Model No. 950
DONKEY FOAL

Designer: Arthur Gredington
Height: 5", 12.7 cm
Colour: Grey-brown - gloss
Issued: 1941-1962

Description:	U.K. £	U.S. $	Can. $
Gloss	75.00	125.00	175.00

Model No. 1035
GOAT

Designer:	Arthur Gredington
Height:	5 1/2", 14.0 cm
Colour:	Tan - gloss
Issued:	1945-1971
Set:	1036

Price	*U.K. £*	*U.S. $*	*Can. $*
Gloss	125.00	200.00	275.00

Model No. 1036
KID

Designer:	Arthur Gredington
Height:	2 1/2", 6.4 cm
Colour:	Tan - gloss
Issued:	1945-1971
Set:	1035

Price	*U.K. £*	*U.S. $*	*Can. $*
Gloss	95.00	150.00	225.00

Photograph not
available at press time

Model No. 1364A
DONKEY
Version One

Designer:	Mr. Orwell
Height:	4 1/2", 11.9 cm
Colour:	Natural - gloss
Issued:	1955-1955

Description:	*U.K. £*	*U.S. $*	*Can. $*
Gloss		Extremely Rare	

Model No. 1364B
DONKEY
Version Two

Designer:	Mr. Orwell
Height:	4 1/2", 11.9 cm
Colour:	Natural - gloss or matt
Issued:	1: Gloss - 1955 to the present
	2: Matt - 1987-1989

Description:	*U.K. £*	*U.S. $*	*Can. $*
1: Gloss	14.95	N/A	N/A
2: Matt	45.00	75.00	100.00

Model No. 1452A
SOW CH "WALL QUEEN 40TH"

Designer:	Arthur Gredington
Height:	2 3/4", 7.0 cm
Colour:	White - gloss or matt
Issued:	1: Gloss - 1956 to the present
	2: Matt - 1987-1989

Description:	U.K. £	U.S. $	Can. $
1: Gloss	14.95	N/A	N/A
2: Matt	25.00	40.00	60.00

Photograph not
available at press time

Model No. 1452B
SOW - on wooden plinth

Designer:	Arthur Gredington
Height:	3 3/4", 9.5 cm
Colour:	White - gloss
Issued:	1993 to the present

Description:	U.K. £	U.S. $	Can. $
Gloss	17.95	N/A	N/A

Model No. 1453A
BOAR Ch. "WALL CHAMPION BOY 53RD"

Designer:	Arthur Gredington
Height:	2 3/4", 7.0 cm
Colour:	White - gloss or matt
Issued:	1: Gloss - 1956 to the present
	2: Matt - 1987-1989

Description:	U.K. £	U.S. $	Can. $
1: Gloss	14.95	N/A	N/A
2: Matt	25.00	40.00	60.00

Photograph not
available at press time

Model No. 1453B
BOAR - on wooden plinth

Designer:	Arthur Gredington
Height:	3 3/4", 9.5 cm
Colour:	White - gloss
Issued:	1993 to the present

Description:	U.K. £	U.S. $	Can. $
Gloss	17.95	N/A	N/A

Model No. 1511
WESSEX SADDLEBACK SOW
 "MERRYWOOD SILVER WINGS 56TH

Designer:	Colin Melbourne
Height:	2 3/4", 7.0 cm
Colour:	Black and white - gloss
Issued:	1957-1969
Set:	1512

Description:	U.K. £	U.S. $	Can. $
Gloss	225.00	350.00	500.00

Model No. 1512
WESSEX SADDLEBACK BOAR
"FARACRE VISCOUNT 3RD"

Designer:	Colin Melbourne
Height:	2 3/4", 7.0 cm
Colour:	Black and white - gloss
Issued:	1957-1969
Set:	1511

Description:	U.K. £	U.S. $	Can. $
Gloss	225.00	350.00	500.00.

Model No. 1760
PIGGY BANK

Designer:	Albert Hallam
Height:	8 1/2", 21.6 cm
Colour:	White, grey and pink - gloss
Issued:	1961-1967
Series:	Fun Models

Description:	U.K. £	U.S. $	Can. $
Various - gloss	75.00	125.00	165.00

Model No. 1765
BLACK FACED SHEEP

Designer:	Mr. Garbet
Height:	3 1/4", 8.3 cm
Colour:	Black and white - gloss or matt
Modelled:	1961
Issued:	1: Gloss - 1963 to the present
	2: Matt - 1987-1989
Set:	1828

Description:	U.K. £	U.S. $	Can. $
1: Gloss	11.50	N/A	N/A
2: Matt	25.00	40.00	60.00

Model No. 1765/1828
BLACK FACED SHEEP AND LAMB
- on wooden plinth

Designer:	Mr. Garbet and Arthur Gredington
Height:	3 3/4", 9.5 cm
Colour:	Black and white - gloss
Issued:	1993 to the present

Description:	U.K. £	U.S. $	Can. $
Gloss	24.95	N/A	N/A

Note: Sheep is no. 1765; Lamb is no. 1828.

Model No. 1828
BLACK FACED LAMB

Designer:	Arthur Gredington
Height:	2 1/2", 6.4 cm
Colour:	Black and white - gloss or matt
Modelled:	1962
Issued:	1: Gloss - 1963 to the present
	2: Matt - 1987-1989
Set:	1765

Description:	U.K. £	U.S. $	Can. $
1: Gloss	6.95	N/A	N/A
2: Matt	25.00	40.00	50.00

Model No. 1917
MERINO RAM

Designer:	Arthur Gredington
Height:	4 1/4", 10.8 cm
Colour:	Grey with white face - gloss
Modelled:	1963
Issued:	1964-1967

Description:	U.K. £	U.S. $	Can. $
Gloss	350.00	550.00	750.00

Model No. 2103
LAUGHING PIGS

Designer:	Albert Hallam
Height:	2 3/4", 7.0 cm
Colour:	White and pink - gloss
Modelled:	1967
Issued:	1968-1971
Series:	Fun Models

Description:	U.K. £	U.S. $	Can. $
Gloss	125.00	200.00	275.00

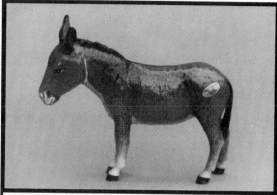

Model No. 2110
DONKEY FOAL

Designer:	Graham Tongue
Height:	4 1/2", 11.9 cm
Colour:	Grey-brown - gloss or matt
Modelled:	1967
Issued:	1: Gloss - 1968 to the present
	2: Matt - 1987-1989

Description:	U.K. £	U.S. $	Can. $
1: Gloss	11.50	N/A	N/A
2: Matt	25.00	40.00	55.00

Model No. 2267
DONKEY

Designer:	Albert Hallam and Graham Tongue
Height:	5 1/2", 14.0 cm
Colour:	Grey-brown - gloss or matt
Modelled:	1969
Issued:	1: Gloss - 1970 to the present
	2: Matt - 1987-1989

Description:	U.K. £	U.S. $	Can. $
1: Gloss	16.50	N/A	N/A
2: Matt	25.00	40.00	55.00

Photograph not
available at press time

Model No. 2294
PIGLET CANDLESTICK

Designer:	Harry Sales
Length:	11" x 3 1/2", 27.9 x 8.9 cm
Colour:	1: Blue and white - gloss
	2: Brown glaze
Modelled:	1969
Issued:	1970-1973
Series:	Fun Models

Description:	U.K. £	U.S. $	Can. $
1: Blue/white	75.00	125.00	175.00
2: Brown glaze	75.00	125.00	175.00

Note: This candlestick has four candle holders.

Model No. 2746
PIG AND PIGLET "Piggy Back"

Designer:	Graham Tongue
Length:	6 1/2", 16.5 cm
Colour:	Pink and white - gloss
Modelled:	1981
Issued:	1983-1994
Series:	Fun Models

Description:	U.K. £	U.S. $	Can. $
Gloss	45.00	75.00	100.00

Model No. 3071
BLACK-FACED RAM

Designer:	Mr. Chawner
Height:	3 1/4", 8.3 cm
Colour:	Black and white - gloss or matt
Modelled:	1987
Issued:	1: Gloss - 1988 to the present
	2: Matt - 1988-1989

Description:	U.K. £	U.S. $	Can. $
Gloss	16.50	N/A	N/A
Matt	25.00	40.00	55.00

Model No. 3071/1765
"EWE AND I" - on ceramic base

Designer:	Unknown
Height:	4 1/2",11.9 cm
Base:	7 1/2", 19.1 cm
Colour:	Black and white - gloss
Issued:	Unknown

Description:	U.K. £	U.S. $	Can. $
Gloss	75.00	125.00	175.00

Note: Ram is no. 3071; Sheep is no. 1765.
Produced as a special commission.

Chapter Six

FISH

All but one of these fish models are realistically portrayed. The detail on many of them is amazing, for example the Golden Trout. So many colours were used, and the result is simply stunning.

The only stylized version of a fish is one from the *Moda* series. All the rest are supported on bases, although their fins are still vulnerable to damage. Very few, therefore, have survived intact to the present, and as a result they are particularly hard to find in mint condition, although restored ones do appear.

INDEX BY MODEL NUMBER

Model No. 1032

TROUT

Designer: Arthur Gredington
Height: 6 1/4", 15.9 cm
Colours: Brown and dark green - gloss
Issued: 1945-1975

Model No.	Price U.K. £	U.S. $	Can. $
1032	125.00	200.00	225.00

Model No. 1047

ANGEL FISH

Designer: Arthur Gredington
Colours: Silver, red and green-brown - gloss
Height: 7 1/4", 18.4 cm
Issued: 1946-1967

Model No.	Price U.K. £	U.S. $	Can. $
1047	145.00	250.00	375.00

Model No. 1232

OCEANIC BONITO

Designer: Arthur Gredington
Colours: Blue, silver and green - gloss
Height: 7 1/4", 18.4 cm
Issued: 1952-1968

Model		Price	
No.	U.K. £	U.S. $	Can. $
1232	165.00	275.00	400.00

Model No 1233

ATLANTIC SALMON

Designer: Arthur Gredington
Colours: Blue, silver and green - gloss
Height: 6 1/2", 16.5 cm
Issued: 1952-1970

Model		Price	
No.	U.K. £	U.S. $	Can. $
1233	135.00	225.00	350.00

Model No. 1235

BARRACUDA

Designer: Arthur Gredington
Colours: Blue and silver

Model No.	Finish	Height	Intro.	Disc.	U.K. £	Price U.S. $	Can. $
1235	Gloss	4 3/4", 12.1 cm	1952	1968	195.00	325.00	400.00

Model No: 1243

MARLIN

Designer: Arthur Gredington
Colours: Blue, grey and green

Note: Illustration Courtesy of Royal Doulton

Model No.	Finish	Height	Intro.	Disc.	U.K. £	Price U.S. $	Can. $
1243	Gloss	5 1/2", 14.0 cm	1952	1970	225.00	350.00	450.00

Model No: 1246

GOLDEN TROUT

Designer: Arthur Gredington
Colours: Blue, yellow and green

Model No.	Finish	Height	Intro.	Disc.	U.K. £	Price U.S. $	Can. $
1246	Gloss	6", 15.0 cm	1952	1970	125.00	200.00	250.00

Model No. 1266

LARGE-MOUTHED BLACK BASS

Designer: Arthur Gredington
Colours: Yellow, black, beige and blue

Model No.	Finish	Height	Intro.	Disc.	U.K. £	Price U.S. $	Can. $
1266	Gloss	5", 12.7 cm	1952	1968	165.00	275.00	350.00

Model No. 1390

TROUT

Designer: Arthur Gredington
Colours: Brown and dark green - gloss
Height: 4", 10.1 cm
Issued: 1955-1975

Model		Price	
No.	U.K. £	U.S. $	Can. $
1390	125.00	200.00	225.00

Model No. 1485

BLACK BASS

Designer: Colin Melbourne
Colours: Brown and dark green - gloss
Height: 6", 15.0 cm
Issued: 1957-1968

Model		Price	
No.	U.K. £	U.S. $	Can. $
1485	145.00	225.00	275.00

Note: Illustration courtesy of Royal Doulton.

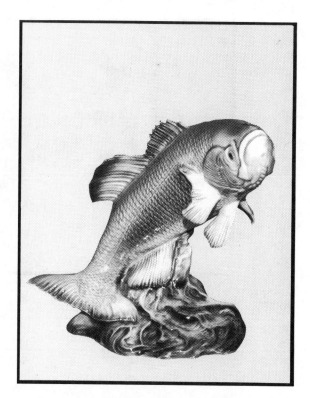

Model No. 1599

TROUT (Ash Bowl)

Designer: Graham Tongue
Colours: Brown fish, turquoise-blue bowl
Heigth: 5", 12.7 cm
Issued: 1959-1971

Model No.	Price U.K. £	U.S. $	Can. $
2087	110.00	175.00	250.00

Model No. 1874

ROACH

Designer: Arthur Gredington
Colours: Turquoise and browns

Model No.	Finish	Length	Intro.	Disc.	U.K. £	Price U.S. $	Can. $
1874	Gloss	6 1/4", 15.9 cm	1963	1971	145.00	235.00	275.00

Model No. 1875

PERCH

Designer: Arthur Gredington
Colours: Greens and browns

Model No.	Finish	Length	Intro.	Disc.	U.K. £	Price U.S. $	Can. $
1875	Gloss	6 1/4", 15.9 cm	1963	1971	145.00	225.00	300.00

Model No. 2066

SALMON

Designer: Graham Tongue
Colours: Browns and silver - gloss
Height: 8", 20.3 cm
Issued: 1966-1975

Model No.	U.K. £	Price U.S. $	Can. $
2066	165.00	260.00	350.00

Model No. 2087

TROUT

Designer: Graham Tongue
Colours: Brown with red-brown spots - gloss
Height: 6", 15.0 cm
Issued: 1967-1975

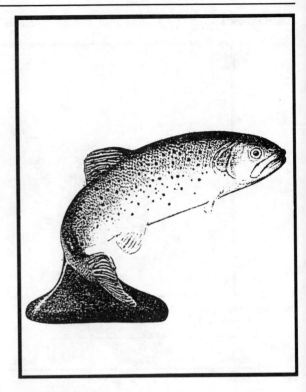

Model		Price	
No.	U.K. £	U.S. $	Can. $
2087	145.00	225.00	275.00

Model No: 2254

FISH (Stylized Model)

Designer: Harry Sales
Colours: Dark and light blue
Series: Moda

Model						Price	
No.	Finish	Height	Intro.	Disc.	U.K. £	U.S. $	Can. $
2254	Gloss	4 1/2", 11.9 cm	1968	1971	110.00	175.00	275.00

Chapter Seven

HORSES

Beswick is most readily associated with the production of accurately modelled horses. Indeed horses form the largest section by far of all the Beswick range. From 1939 to 1989, Beswick produced over 150 different horse models, the vast majority available in several colourways and in gloss or matt finishes. Although each model had a shape number, many were only listed in price lists and catalogues as "horse," "mare" or "foal," which left less knowledgeable collectors and dealers with a considerable identification problem! Some horses do have their names incorporated into their backstamp (for example, the Mountain and Moorland ponies) or numbers imprinted into their base (such as the "lying down foal," 915), and of course those with riders are easy to sort out. But those that remain need careful examination to determine exactly which models they are.

A further consideration is colour. Initially Beswick produced horses in dark chestnut, light brown, dark brown, rocking-horse grey and even in blue gloss. Later brown, painted white, opaque, palomino, chestnut and light grey glosses were added to the range, and most of the initial colourways were dropped. Special colours were also used for specific models, such as on the 2282 Fjord. From 1970 onwards, matt finishes were introduced in various colours: brown, grey, palomino, white and black. Within each colour there can be considerable variations, from a light tone with shading to an all-over, solid, one-tone version of the same colour. Avid collectors will value the former, which usually indicates an earlier example, painted when more attention was paid to details like well-painted eyes and pink mouths.

The Beswick stable comprises the full spectrum of the equine world, from children's ponies, specific breeds, famous racehorses, to the giant Shires, whilst the *Colin Melbourne* series adds a contemporary touch to the collection.

Arthur Gredington modelled Beswick's first realistic horse in 1939 when he modelled the first version of the 1938 Derby winner, "Bois Roussel". Although a handful of other modellers made contributions to the horse models it was Arthur Gredington who was responsible for the vast majority until he retired in 1968. Graham Tongue then took over, adding many more horses to the range, including a new bronze finish for the "Britannia Series". In August 1989 all except three Beswick horses became "Doulton Animals" and so from that date, although they continued to be produced in the Beswick factory, they were backstamped with the name of the parent company, Royal Doulton. In 1994 to mark the Beswick Centenary it was a horse model that was chosen as a special piece to represent Beswick. This was the large rearing model of "Downland Cancara". Graham Tongue modelled this magnificent horse. In 1995 Cancara was issued with a Royal Doulton backstamp and the three remaining Beswick horses were completely withdrawn, thus sadly, marking the end of an era for Beswick horses.

Note: DA numbers are given for easy cross-reference with the Charlton Standard Catalogue of Royal Doulton Animals.

Model No. 701

"BOIS ROUSSEL"
RACEHORSE

There are two varieties of "Bois Roussell". The first version was introduced in 1939.

FIRST VERSION : *The tail is attached to the hind legs all the way down and the legs are long and thick.*

Designer: Arthur Gredington
Height: 8", 20.3 cm

Colourway	Finish	DA #	Intro.	Discon.	U.K. £	U.S. $	Can. $
Blue	Gloss		1939	1947			
Light brown	Gloss		1940	1947			
Dark brown	Gloss		1940	1947	Extremely Rare		
Dark chestnut	Gloss		1939	1947			
Rocking horse grey	Gloss		c.1940	1947			

SECOND VERSION: *In 1947 Bois Roussel was re-modelled with only the tail-end attached to the leg.*

Colourway	Finish	DA #	Intro.	Discon.	U.K. £	U.S. $	Can. $
Brown	Gloss	42	1947	1989	65.00	100.00	150.00
Brown	Matt	42	1979	1989	65.00	100.00	150.00
Chestnut	Gloss	—	1958	1967	200.00	325.00	450.00
Grey	Gloss	42	1960	1989	95.00	150.00	225.00
Grey	Matt	—	1970	1989	85.00	130.00	200.00
Opaque	Gloss	—	1960	1967	125.00	200.00	275.00
Painted white	Gloss	—	1952	1967	150.00	250.00	350.00
Palomino	Gloss	—	1960	1989	95.00	150.00	225.00
Palomino	Matt	—	1970	1983	150.00	250.00	350.00
Rocking horse grey	Gloss	—	1947	1962	225.00	375.00	500.00
White	Matt	—	1970	1982	100.00	150.00	225.00

SERIES: On ceramic stand or wooden plinths.

The stand was shape no. 1809, modelled by Albert Hallam in 1963.

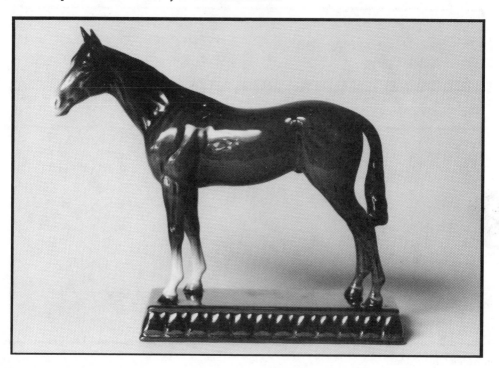

Colourway/stand/finish	Intro.	Discon.	U.K. £	U.S. $	Can. $
Brown/brown ceramic/gloss	c.1963	Unknown		Rare	
Brown/copper lustre ceramic/gloss	c.1963	Unknown		Rare	
Chestnut/ceramic/gloss	c.1988	Unknown		Rare	

Model No. 728

FOAL
(Comical Type)

Designer: Arthur Gredington
Height: 5", 12.7 cm

Colourway	Finish	Intro.	Disc.	U.K. £	U.S. $	Can. $
Blue	Gloss	1939	1954	150.00	250.00	350.00
Brown	Gloss	1940	1971	35.00	55.00	75.00
Chestnut	Gloss	1958	1966	125.00	200.00	275.00
Dark chestnut	Gloss	1939	1954		Rare	
Grey	Gloss	1961	1971	65.00	100.00	150.00
Opaque	Gloss	1961	1971	65.00	100.00	150.00
Painted white	Gloss	1961	1966	125.00	200.00	275.00
Palomino	Gloss	1961	1971	85.00	135.00	200.00
Rocking horse grey	Gloss	c.1940	1962	150.00	250.00	350.00
Stone/ivory	Satin	Unknown	1954		Rare	
White	Matt	1970	1970		Rare	

Model No. 763/1421

FOAL
(Small, Stretched, Upright)

First Version: Long ears   Second Version: Short ears

Designer: Arthur Gredington
Height: 3 1/2", 8.9 cm

FIRST VERSION: *Long ears, thick legs. When viewed from the back legs almost touch. Tail straight.*

Colourway	Finish	Intro.	Disc.	U.K. £	U.S. $	Can. $
Blue	Gloss	1940	Unknown	150.00	250.00	350.00
Brown	Gloss	1940	Unknown	45.00	70.00	95.00
Rocking horse grey	Gloss	c.1940	Unknown	150.00	250.00	350.00

SECOND VERSION: *Short ears, thick legs, but an overall smaller model. Tail is straight.*

Colourway	Finish	Intro.	Disc.	U.K. £	U.S. $	Can. $
Blue	Gloss	Unknown	1956	150.00	250.00	350.00
Brown	Gloss	Unknown	1956	45.00	70.00	95.00
Rocking horse grey	Gloss	Unknown	1956	150.00	250.00	350.00

THIRD VERSION: *Very thin legs with off hind stretched out well behind the near hind. Tail is slightly bent.*

In 1956 model no. 763 was completely remodelled by Arthur Gredington, but the model no. 763 was retained.

Colourway	Finish	Intro.	Disc.	U.K. £	U.S. $	Can. $
Brown	Gloss	1956	1976	45.00	70.00	95.00
Chestnut	Gloss	1958	1967	110.00	150.00	250.00
Grey	Gloss	1961	1976	50.00	80.00	110.00
Opaque	Gloss	1961	1973	55.00	85.00	120.00
Painted white	Gloss	1962	1967	110.00	175.00	250.00
Palomino	Gloss	1956	1976	55.00	85.00	120.00
Rocking horse grey	Gloss	1956	1961	175.00	275.00	400.00
White	Matt	1970	1976	75.00	125.00	175.00

Model No. 766

FOAL - TROTTING
(With Or Without Base)

Photograph not
available at press time

Designer: Arthur Gredington
Height: 3 3/4", 9.5 cm

VARIATION No. 1:   Free standing

Colourway	Finish	Intro.	Disc.	U.K. £	U.S. $	Can. $
Blue	Gloss	1940	By 1954		Extremely Rare	
Light brown	Gloss	1940	By 1954		Extremely Rare	
Dark brown	Gloss	1940	By 1954		Extremely Rare	
Dark chestnut	Gloss	1940	By 1954		Extremely Rare	

VARIATION No. 2:   On ceramic base

Colourway	Finish	Intro.	Disc.	U.K. £	U.S. $	Can. $
Blue	Gloss	1940	By 1954		Extremely Rare	
Light brown	Gloss	1940	By 1954		Extremely Rare	
Dark brown	Gloss	1940	By 1954		Extremely Rare	
Dark chestnut	Gloss	1940	By 1954		Extremely Rare	

Model No. 815

FOAL
(Small, Stretched, Facing Right)

Designer: Arthur Gredington
Height: 3 1/4", 8.3 cm

Colourway	Finsh	DA #	Intro.	Disc.	U.K. £	U.S. $	Can. $
Blue	Gloss	—	1940	1954	125.00	200.00	300.00
Brown	Gloss	74	1940	1989	30.00	50.00	75.00
Brown	Matt	74	1979	1989	35.00	55.00	85.00
Chestnut	Gloss	—	1958	1967	100.00	150.00	200.00
Dark chestnut	Gloss	—	1940	1954	Extremely Rare		
Grey	Gloss	74	1961	1989	60.00	95.00	125.00
Opaque	Gloss	—	1961	1973	65.00	100.00	125.00
Painted white	Gloss	—	1962	1967	100.00	150.00	225.00
Palomino	Gloss	—	1961	1989	50.00	75.00	100.00
Rocking horse grey	Gloss	—	c.1940	1962	125.00	200.00	275.00
White	Matt	—	1970	1982	65.00	100.00	125.00

Model No. 701 "Bois Roussel" Racehorse

Second Version
Brown Gloss

Second Version
Brown Matt

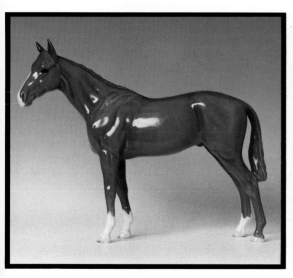

Model 701
"Bois Roussel" Racehorse
Second Version - Chestnut Gloss

Model No. 1033
Shetland Pony
Chestnut Gloss

Model No. 701 "Bois Roussel" Racehorse

<table>
<tr><td align="center">Second Version
Grey Gloss</td><td align="center">Second Version
Grey Matt</td></tr>
</table>

Model No. 701 "Bois Roussel" Racehorse

<table>
<tr><td align="center">Second Version
Palomino Gloss</td><td align="center">Second Version
Palomino Matt</td></tr>
</table>

Model No. 701 "Bois Roussel" Racehorse

**Second Version
Painted White Gloss**

**Second Version
White Matt**

**Model No. 701
"Bois Roussel" Racehorse
Second Version - Opaque Gloss**

**Model No. 1361
Hackney
Rocking Horse Grey Gloss**

Model No. 763, Foal
First Version - Blue Gloss

Model No. 2914, Spirit of Earth
Bronze Glaze
Britannia Series

Model No. 1359, Suffolk Punch
Colourway Variations
Dark Chestnut Gloss, Light Chestnut Gloss

Model No. 1771, Arab "Bahram"
Grey Gloss

Model No. 818   *SHIRE MARE*

In recognition of 50 years of production of model number 818 a black gloss shire mare was commissioned by the Beswick Collectors Circle in 1990. Approximately 135 of these were issued with a gold backstamp for Circle Members.

Designer: Arthur Gredington
Height: 8 1/2"

VARIATION No. 1:	*Colourway:*	*Black gloss with yellow ribbon*
VARIATION No. 2:	*Colourway:*	*Black gloss with blue and yellow ribbon in mane; B.C.C. / Beswick gold backstamp*

Colourway	Finish	DA#	Intro.	Disc.	U.K. £	U.S. $	Can. $
Black - yellow ribbon	Gloss	—	Unknown	Unknown		Rare	
Black - blue/yellow ribbons - Gloss		—	1990	1990	175.00	275.00	400.00
Brown	Gloss	43	1940	1989	60.00	95.00	150.00
Brown	Matt	43	1979	1989	60.00	95.00	150.00
Chestnut	Gloss	—	1958	1967	175.00	275.00	400.00
Grey	Gloss	—	1961	1989	80.00	125.00	200.00
Opaque	Gloss	—	1961	1973	95.00	150.00	225.00
Painted white	Gloss	—	1961	1970	175.00	275.00	400.00
Palomino	Gloss	—	1961	1973	175.00	275.00	400.00
Piebald	Gloss	—	Unknown	Unknown	250.00	400.00	550.00
Rockinghorse grey	Gloss	—	c.1940	1962	175.00	275.00	400.00
Skewbald	Gloss	—	Unknown	Unknown	275.00	425.00	600.00
White	Matt	—	1970	1982	80.00	125.00	200.00

      VARIATION No. 2:   *Dressed, Series: Harnessed horses*

Colourway	Finish	Intro.	Disc.	U.K. £	U.S. $	Can. $
Brown	Gloss	1974	1982	125.00	200.00	275.00
Grey	Gloss	1974	1982	135.00	225.00	300.00

Model No. 836

FOAL
(Large, Stretched)

First Version: Parallel fore legs

Second Version: Splayed fore legs

Designer: Arthur Gredington
Height: 5", 12.7 cm

FIRST VERSION: *Parallel fore legs*

Colourway	Finish	Intro.	Disc.	U.K. £	U.S. $	Can. $
Brown	Gloss	1940	Unknown	55.00	85.00	125.00
Brown	Matt	1979	Unknown	55.00	85.00	125.00
Chestnut	Gloss	1961	Unknown	110.00	175.00	250.00
Grey	Gloss	1961	Unknown	75.00	125.00	170.00
Opaque	Gloss	1961	Unknown	75.00	125.00	170.00
Painted white	Gloss	1961	Unknown	110.00	175.00	250.00
Palomino	Gloss	1961	Unknown	55.00	85.00	125.00
Rocking horse grey	Gloss	1961	Unknown	180.00	275.00	400.00
White	Matt	1970	Unknown	95.00	150.00	200.00

SECOND VERSION: *Splayed fore legs*

Colourway	Finish	Intro.	Disc.	U.K. £	U.S. $	Can. $
Brown	Gloss	Unknown	1984	45.00	75.00	100.00
Brown	Matt	Unknown	1984	45.00	75.00	100.00
Chestnut	Gloss	Unknown	1967	95.00	150.00	200.00
Grey	Gloss	Unknown	1983	65.00	100.00	150.00
Opaque	Gloss	Unknown	1973	65.00	100.00	150.00
Painted white	Gloss	Unknown	1967	95.00	150.00	200.00
Palomino	Gloss	Unknown	1984	45.00	75.00	100.00
Rocking horse grey	Gloss	Unknown	1962	160.00	250.00	350.00
White	Matt	Unknown	1982	85.00	135.00	175.00

Model No. 855   *STOCKY JOGGING MARE*

FIRST VERSION : *Modelled September 1940. Near fore leg is raised off the ground, near hind leg is under the body. Tail attached to the leg all the way down. Legs rather crudely modelled.*

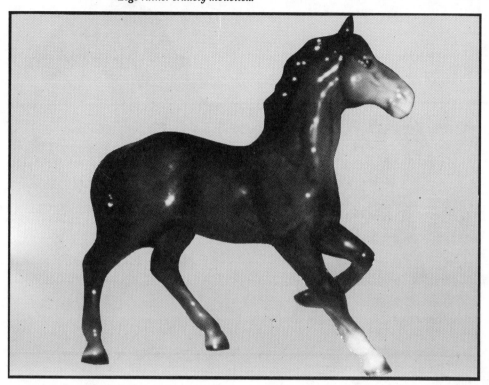

Designer: Arthur Gredington
Height: 6", 5.0 cm

Colourway	Finish	Intro.	Disc.	U.K. £	U.S. $	Can. $
Blue	Gloss	1940	1941			
Dark brown	Gloss	1940	1941			
Light brown	Gloss	1940	1941		Extremely Rare	
Dark chestnut	Gloss	1940	1941			

SECOND VERSION: *Modelled September 1941. Near fore leg is raised off the ground, near hind leg is under the body. Tail arched away from the leg. More shape to the joints of the legs.*

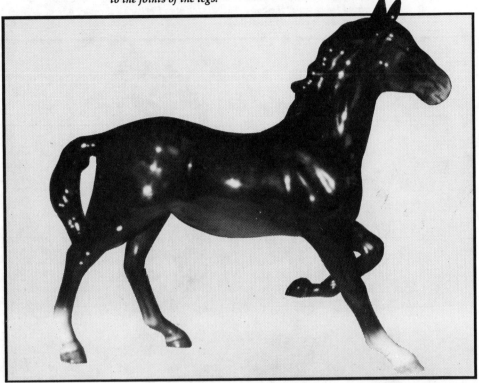

Colourway	Finish	Intro.	Disc.	U.K. £	U.S. $	Can. $
Blue	Gloss	1941	1947			
Dark brown	Gloss	1941	1947			
Light brown	Gloss	1941	1947	Extremely Rare		
Dark chestnut	Gloss	1941	1947			
Rocking horse grey	Gloss	1941	1947			

THIRD VERSION :   *Shape no. 1090 was modelled in 1947 but retained the number 855.*
Off fore leg raised from the ground, off hind leg under the body.
Tail more arched from the body. Head lowered. A "chunkier" model.

Colourway	Finish	DA #	Intro.	Disc.	U.K. £	U.S. $	Can. $
Blue	Gloss	—	1947	Unknown	175.00	275.00	400.00
Brown	Gloss	44	1947	1989	65.00	100.00	150.00
Chestnut	Gloss	—	1958	1967	175.00	275.00	400.00
Grey	Gloss	—	1961	1989	65.00	100.00	150.00
Opaque	Gloss	—	1961	1973	90.00	150.00	200.00
Painted white	Gloss	—	1961	1967	175.00	275.00	400.00
Palomino	Gloss	—	1961	1989	65.00	100.00	150.00
Rocking horse grey	Gloss	—	c.1947	1962	195.00	300.00	450.00
White	Matt	—	1970	1982	90.00	150.00	200.00

Model No. 868

HUNTSMAN
(On Rearing Horse)

STYLE ONE: *On rearing horse*

FIRST VERSION: *Huntsman is sitting straight up and his lower legs are also vertical.*
His coat is cut away at the waist. He is riding a common headed horse.

Designer: Arthur Gredington
Height: 10", 25.4 cm

COLOURWAY No. 1:   *Orangey red coat, cream breeches.*

Colourway	Finish	Intro.	Disc.	U.K. £	U.S. $	Can. $
Brown	Gloss	1940	1952	300.00	475.00	650.00
Dark Chestnut	Gloss	1940	1952		Extremely Rare	
Rocking horse grey	Gloss	c.1940	1952		Extremely Rare	

COLOURWAY No. 2:   *Scarlet coat and white breeches.*

Colourway	Finish	Intro.	Disc.	U.K. £	U.S. $	Can. $
Brown	Gloss	1940	1952	275.00	450.00	600.00
Rocking horse grey	Gloss	c.1948	1952		Extremely Rare	

SECOND VERSION: *Huntsman is leaning back slightly. His coat is not cut away at the waist.*
The horse's head has an Arab appearance (dished profile).

Colourway	Finish	Intro.	Disc.	U.K. £	U.S. $	Can. $
Brown	Gloss	1952	1995	100.00	150.00	250.00
Chestnut	Gloss	1958	1967	300.00	475.00	650.00
Grey	Gloss	1962	1972	275.00	450.00	600.00
Opaque	Gloss	1971	1973	175.00	275.00	400.00
Painted white	Gloss	1965	1971	250.00	400.00	550.00
Palomino	Gloss	1961	1972	275.00	450.00	600.00
Rocking horse grey	Gloss	1952	1962	Extremely Rare		

SERIES: *Britannia Series*

Colourway	Finish	Intro.	Disc.	U.K. £	U.S. $	Can. $
Bronze	Satin	1989	1993	100.00	150.00	225.00

Model No. 915

FOAL
(Lying)

Designer: Arthur Gredington
Height: 3 1/4", 8.3 cm

Colourway	Finish	DA #	Intro.	Disc.	U.K. £	U.S. $	Can. $
Brown	Gloss	75	1941	1989	40.00	65.00	85.00
Brown	Matt	75	1979	1989	40.00	65.00	85.00
Chestnut	Gloss	—	1958	1967	125.00	200.00	275.00
Grey	Gloss	75	1961	1989	45.00	75.00	100.00
Opaque	Gloss	—	1961	1973	75.00	125.00	165.00
Painted white	Gloss	—	1962	1967	100.00	150.00	225.00
Palomino	Gloss	—	1961	1989	45.00	75.00	100.00
Rocking horse grey	Gloss	—	c.1942	1962	175.00	275.00	400.00
White	Matt	—	1970	1982	75.00	125.00	165.00

Model No. 939   *GIRL ON JUMPING HORSE*

The horse used for model 939 is also that used for model 982 "Huntswoman"

Designer: Arthur Gredington
Height: 9 3/4", 24.7 cm

Colourway	Finish	Intro.	Disc.	U.K. £	U.S. $	Can. $
Brown	Gloss	1941	1965	250.00	400.00	550.00

Model No. 946

FOAL
(Grazing)

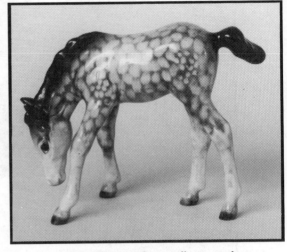

First Version: Off-side hooves almost touch

Second Version: Legs well separated

Designer: Arthur Gredington
Height: 3 1/4", 8.3 cm

FIRST VERSION: *Has common head and the off-side hooves almost touch.*

Colourway	Finish	Intro.	Disc.	U.K. £	U.S. $	Can. $
Light brown	Gloss	1941	1955	55.00	85.00	125.00
Dark brown	Gloss	1941	1955	55.00	85.00	125.00
Rocking horse grey	Gloss	1941	1955	175.00	275.00	400.00

SECOND VERSION: *Much finer head with the legs being well separated.*

Colourway	Finish	DA #	Intro.	Disc.	U.K. £	U.S. $	Can. $
Brown	Gloss	76	1955	1989	30.00	50.00	70.00
Brown	Matt	76	1979	1989	30.00	50.00	70.00
Chestnut	Gloss	—	1958	1967	125.00	200.00	275.00
Grey	Gloss	76	1961	1989	35.00	55.00	75.00
Opaque	Gloss	—	1961	1967	95.00	150.00	200.00
Painted white	Gloss	—	1961	1967	125.00	200.00	275.00
Palomino	Gloss	76	1961	1989	35.00	55.00	75.00
Rocking horse grey	Gloss	—	1955	1962	150.00	250.00	325.00
White	Matt	—	1970	1982	55.00	85.00	125.00

Model No. 947

FOAL
(Large, Head Down)

Designer: Arthur Gredington
Height: 4 1/2", 11.9 cm

Colourway	Finish	DA #	Intro.	Disc.	U.K. £	U.S. $	Can. $
Brown	Gloss	77	1941	1989	35.00	55.00	75.00
Brown	Matt	77	1979	1989	35.00	55.00	75.00
Chestnut	Gloss	—	1958	1967	125.00	200.00	275.00
Grey	Gloss	—	1961	1983	55.00	85.00	125.00
Opaque	Gloss	—	1961	1973	75.00	125.00	175.00
Painted white	Gloss	—	1962	1967	125.00	200.00	275.00
Palomino	Gloss	—	1961	1983	55.00	85.00	125.00
Rocking horse grey	Gloss	—	c.1942	1962	150.00	250.00	350.00
White	Matt	—	1970	1982	75.00	125.00	175.00

Model No. 951

SHIRE FOAL
(Large)

Designer: Arthur Gredington
Height: 6 1/4", 15.9 cm

Colourway	Finish	Intro.	Disc.	U.K. £	U.S. $	Can. $
Blue	Gloss	1941	Unknown		Rare	
Brown	Gloss	1941	1971	60.00	95.00	125.00
Chestnut	Gloss	1958	1967	150.00	250.00	325.00
Grey	Gloss	1961	1971	85.00	135.00	200.00
Opaque	Gloss	1961	1971	75.00	125.00	165.00
Painted white	Gloss	1962	1967	150.00	250.00	325.00
Palomino	Gloss	1961	1971	95.00	150.00	210.00
Rocking horse grey	Gloss	1941	1962	175.00	275.00	400.00
White	Matt	1970	1970	95.00	150.00	210.00

Model No. 953

MARE AND FOAL ON BASE

The mare is a modern 976 with the foal and the base varying.

FIRST VERSION : *The foal has its tail and near fore leg slightly raised.*
The base was rectangular.

Designer: Arthur Gredington
Height: 7 3/4", 19.7 cm

Colourway	Finish	Intro.	Disc.	U.K. £	U.S. $	Can. $
Brown	Gloss	1941	1949			
Rocking horse grey	Gloss	1941	1949		Extremely Rare	

SECOND VERSION : *Foal has all four legs attached to an irregularly shaped base and the tail hangs straight down.*

Colourway	Finish	Intro.	Disc.	U.K. £	U.S. $	Can. $
Brown	Gloss	1949	1983	100.00	150.00	250.00
Chesnut	Gloss	1958	1967	250.00	400.00	550.00
Grey	Gloss	1958	1972	200.00	325.00	450.00
Opaque	Gloss	1971	1973	175.00	275.00	400.00
Painted white	Gloss	1962	1967	250.00	400.00	550.00
Palomino	Gloss	1958	1972	200.00	325.00	450.00
Rocking horse grey	Gloss	1950	1962	Extremely Rare		
White	Matt	1971	1981	110.00	175.00	250.00

THIRD VERSION : *Foal is model no. 1813, second version, on an irregularly shaped base.*

Colourway	Finish	Intro.	Disc.	U.K. £	U.S. $	Can. $
Brown mare with an orangey bay foal	Gloss	1983	1983		Rare	

Model No. 975   *CANTERING SHIRE*

Designer: Arthur Gredington
Height: 8 3/4", 22.2 cm

Colourway	Finish	DA #	Intro.	Disc.	U.K. £	U.S. $	Can. $
Brown	Gloss	45	1943	1989	65.00	100.00	150.00
Brown	Matt	—	1980	1989	65.00	100.00	150.00
Chestnut	Gloss	—	1958	1967	200.00	325.00	450.00
Grey	Gloss	—	1961	1989	60.00	95.00	135.00
Opaque	Gloss	—	1966	1967	125.00	200.00	275.00
Painted white	Gloss	—	1962	1967	200.00	350.00	450.00
Palomino	Gloss	—	1961	1970	200.00	350.00	450.00
Rocking horse grey	Gloss	—	c.1944	1962	225.00	375.00	500.00
White	Matt	—	1971	1982	90.00	150.00	200.00

Note: Also known in flambé

Model No. 976

MARE
(Facing Left)

The mare used in model 953.

Designer: Arthur Gredington
Height: 6 3/4", 17.2 cm

Colourway	Finish	DA #	Intro.	Disc.	U.K. £	U.S. $	Can. $
Brown	Gloss	46	1941	1989	60.00	95.00	150.00
Brown	Matt	46	1979	1989	70.00	110.00	160.00
Chestnut	Gloss	—	1958	1967	175.00	275.00	400.00
Grey	Gloss	46	1962	1989	60.00	95.00	150.00
Opaque	Gloss	—	1961	1973	80.00	125.00	195.00
Painted white	Gloss	—	1961	1967	175.00	275.00	400.00
Palomino	Gloss	—	1961	1983	75.00	125.00	175.00
Rocking horse grey	Gloss	—	c.1942	1962	200.00	350.00	450.00
White	Matt	—	1970	1982	85.00	135.00	195.00

Model No. 982   *HUNTSWOMAN*

The horse used for model 982 is the same as that used for model 939 "Girl on Jumping Horse".

Designer: Arthur Gredington
Height: 10", 25.4 cm

Colourway	Finish	Intro.	Disc.	U.K. £	U.S. $	Can. $
Brown	Gloss	1942	1967	275.00	475.00	650.00

Model No. 996

FOAL
(Small, Gambolling left)

Designer: Arthur Gredington
Height: 3 1/4", 8.3 cm

Colourway	Finish	Intro.	Disc.	U.K. £	U.S. $	Can. $
Brown	Gloss	1943	1976	50.00	80.00	110.00
Chestnut	Gloss	1958	1967	110.00	175.00	250.00
Grey	Gloss	1961	1976	55.00	85.00	125.00
Opaque	Gloss	1961	1973	65.00	100.00	150.00
Painted white	Gloss	1961	1967	110.00	175.00	250.00
Palomino	Gloss	1961	1976	55.00	85.00	125.00
Rocking horse grey	Gloss	c.1944	1962	150.00	250.00	350.00
White	Matt	1970	1976	75.00	125.00	175.00

Model No. 997

FOAL
(Small, Stretched, Facing Left)

Designer: Arthur Gredington
Height: 3 1/4", 8.3 cm

Colourway	Finish	DA #	Intro.	Disc.	U.K. £	U.S. $	Can. $
Brown	Gloss	78	1943	1989	30.00	50.00	70.00
Brown	Matt	78	1979	1989	30.00	50.00	70.00
Chestnut	Gloss	—	1958	1967	100.00	150.00	250.00
Grey	Gloss	78	1961	1989	35.00	60.00	80.00
Opaque	Gloss	—	1961	1973	45.00	75.00	125.00
Painted white	Gloss	—	1961	1967	100.00	150.00	250.00
Palomino	Gloss	—	1961	1989	30.00	50.00	70.00
Rocking horse grey	Gloss	—	c.1944	1962	125.00	200.00	300.00
White	Matt	—	1970	1982	50.00	75.00	100.00

Model No. 1014

WELSH COB
(Rearing)

FIRST VERSION: **The tail is attached to the ceramic base.**

Designer: Arthur Gredington
Height: 10 1/4", 26.0 cm

Colourway	Finish	Intro.	Disc.	U.K. £	U.S. $	Can. $
Brown	Gloss	1944	Unknown	110.00	175.00	275.00
Chestnut	Gloss	1958	Unknown	250.00	425.00	550.00
Grey	Gloss	1961	Unknown	175.00	275.00	400.00
Opaque	Gloss	1961	Unknown	125.00	200.00	295.00
Painted white	Gloss	1962	Unknown	250.00	425.00	550.00
Palomino	Gloss	1961	Unknown	150.00	250.00	350.00
Rocking horse grey	Gloss	c.1945	Unknown	300.00	500.00	675.00
White	Matt	1970	Unknown	125.00	200.00	295.00

SECOND VERSION: *Tail hangs loose.*

Colourway	Finish	DA #	Intro.	Disc.	U.K. £	U.S. $	Can. $
Brown	Gloss	41	Unknown	1989	95.00	150.00	200.00
Chestnut	Gloss	—	Unknown	1967	200.00	350.00	450.00
Grey	Gloss	—	Unknown	1973	100.00	150.00	200.00
Grey	Matt	—	Unknown	1983	80.00	125.00	175.00
Opaque	Gloss	—	Unknown	1973	100.00	150.00	225.00
Painted white	Gloss	—	Unknown	1967	200.00	350.00	450.00
Palomino	Gloss	—	Unknown	1973	120.00	200.00	275.00
White	Matt	—	Unknown	1983	100.00	150.00	200.00

Model No. 1033

SHETLAND PONY
(Woolly Shetland Mare)

Designer: Arthur Gredington
Height: 5 3/4", 14.6 cm

Colourway	Finish	Intro.	Disc.	U.K. £	U.S. $	Can. $
Brown	Gloss	1945	1989	75.00	125.00	175.00
Chestnut	Gloss	Unknown	Unknown	175.00	275.00	400.00
Dapple grey	Gloss	Unknown	Unknown	175.00	275.00	400.00
Palomino	Gloss	Unknown	Unknown	175.00	275.00	400.00
White	Matt	1973	1982	95.00	150.00	200.00

Model No. 1034

SHETLAND FOAL

Designer: Arthur Gredington
Height: 3 3/4", 9.5 cm

Colourway	Finish	DA #	Intro.	Disc.	U.K. £	U.S. $	Can. $
Brown	Gloss	79	1945	1989	40.00	60.00	90.00
Brown	Matt	79	1979	1989	40.00	60.00	90.00
White	Matt	—	1973	1982	60.00	90.00	110.00

Model No. 1037

RACEHORSE AND JOCKEY
(Walking Racehorse)

The jockey's silks, for an extra payment, could be decorated as the purchaser wished. A great many colourways and number cloths could exist.

Colourway No. 1: Stripes on saddlecloth

Colourway No. 2: Number on saddlecloth

Designer: Arthur Gredington
Height: 8 1/2", 21.6 cm

| | STYLE ONE: | Walking Racehorse |
| | Colourway No. 1: | Stripes on saddlecloth |

Colourway	Finish	Intro.	Disc.	U.K. £	U.S. $	Can. $
Brown	Gloss	1945	Unknown	250.00	400.00	575.00

| | Colourway No. 2: | Number on saddlecloth |

Colourway	Finish	Intro.	Disc.	U.K. £	U.S. $	Can. $
Brown	Gloss	Unknown	1976	225.00	350.00	525.00

Model No. 1050

GRAZING SHIRE

Designer: Arthur Gredington
Height: 5 1/2", 14.0 cm

Colourway	Finish	Intro.	Disc.	U.K. £	U.S. $	Can. $
Brown	Gloss	1946	1970	100.00	150.00	250.00
Chestnut	Gloss	1958	1967	200.00	325.00	450.00
Grey	Gloss	1962	1970	150.00	250.00	350.00
Opaque	Gloss	*1961*	1970	145.00	225.00	350.00
Painted white	Gloss	1962	1967	200.00	325.00	450.00
Palomino	Gloss	*1961*	1970	175.00	275.00	400.00
Rocking horse grey	Gloss	*c.1947*	1962	275.00	450.00	625.00

Model No. 1053

SHIRE FOAL
(Small)

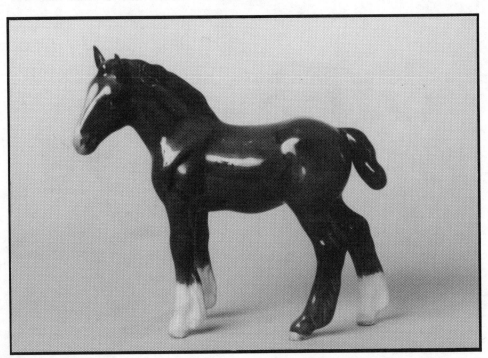

Designer: Arthur Gredington
Height: 5", 12.7 cm

Colourway	Finish	Intro.	Disc.	U.K. £	U.S. $	Can. $
Brown	Gloss	1946	1984	55.00	85.00	125.00
Brown	Matt	1979	1984	55.00	85.00	125.00
Chestnut	Gloss	1958	1967	150.00	250.00	325.00
Grey	Gloss	1961	1973	75.00	125.00	175.00
Opaque	Gloss	1961	1973	95.00	150.00	200.00
Painted white	Gloss	1962	1967	150.00	250.00	325.00
Palomino	Gloss	1961	1973	75.00	125.00	175.00
Rocking horse grey	Gloss	c.1947	1962	175.00	275.00	400.00
White	Matt	1970	1982	100.00	150.00	225.00

Model No. 1084

FOAL
(Medium, Almost Stood Square)

Designer: Arthur Gredington
Height: 4 1/2", 11.9 cm

Colourway	Finish	Intro.	Disc.	U.K. £	U.S. $	Can. $
Brown	Gloss	1947	1984	50.00	75.00	100.00
Brown	Matt	1979	1983	60.00	90.00	125.00
Chestnut	Gloss	1958	1967	125.00	200.00	275.00
Grey	Gloss	1961	1973	65.00	100.00	140.00
Opaque	Gloss	1961	1973	75.00	125.00	175.00
Painted white	Gloss	1961	1967	125.00	200.00	275.00
Palomino	Gloss	1961	1973	65.00	100.00	140.00
Rocking horse grey	Gloss	c.1948	1962	150.00	250.00	350.00
White	Matt	1970	1982	60.00	90.00	125.00

Model No. 1085

FOAL
(Medium, Head Down)

Designer: Arthur Gredington
Height: 3 1/2", 8.9 cm

Colourway	Finish	Intro.	Disc.	U.K. £	U.S. $	Can. $
Brown	Gloss	1947	1971	50.00	75.00	110.00
Chestnut	Gloss	1958	1967	125.00	200.00	275.00
Grey	Gloss	1961	1971	65.00	100.00	150.00
Opaque	Gloss	1961	1971	75.00	125.00	175.00
Painted white	Gloss	1961	1967	125.00	200.00	275.00
Palomino	Gloss	1961	1971	65.00	100.00	150.00
Rocking horse grey	Gloss	c.1948	1962	150.00	250.00	350.00
White	Matt	1970	1970	100.00	150.00	200.00

Model No. 1145

KNIGHT IN ARMOUR
(The Earl of Warwick)

Designer: Arthur Gredington
Height: 10 3/4", 27.8 cm

Colourway	Finish	Intro.	Disc.	U.K. £	U.S. $	Can. $
Grey	Gloss	1949	1973	1,000.00	1,500.00	2,000.00

Model No. 1182

SWISH TAIL HORSE

First Version: The tail is attached to the quarter almost parallel to the ground

Second Version: The tail is slightly lower down and only to the edge of the quarters

Designer: Arthur Gredington
Height: 8 3/4", 22.2 cm

FIRST VERSION: *The tail is attached to the quarters almost parallel to the ground.*

Colourway	Finish	Intro.	Disc.	U.K. £	U.S. $	Can. $
Brown	Gloss	1950	c.1982	75.00	125.00	175.00
Brown	Matt	1970	c.1982	75.00	125.00	175.00
Chestnut	Gloss	1958	1967	175.00	275.00	400.00
Grey	Gloss	1961	c.1982	80.00	125.00	190.00
Grey	Matt	1970	c.1982	80.00	125.00	190.00
Opaque	Gloss	*1961*	1973	95.00	150.00	200.00
Painted white	Gloss	*1961*	1967	175.00	275.00	400.00
Palomino	Gloss	*1961*	c.1982	100.00	150.00	190.00
Palomino	Matt	1970	c.1982	100.00	150.00	190.00
Rocking horse grey	Gloss	*c.1951*	1962	200.00	350.00	475.00
White	Matt	1970	1982	90.00	150.00	200.00

SECOND VERSION: *The tail is attached slightly lower down and only to the edge of the quarters.*

Colourway	Finish	DA #	Intro.	Disc.	U.K. £	U.S. $	Can. $
Brown	Gloss	48	c.1982	1989	60.00	90.00	125.00
Brown	Matt	48	c.1982	1989	60.00	90.00	125.00
Grey	Gloss	—	c.1982	1989	70.00	100.00	150.00
Grey	Matt	—	c.1982	1989	70.00	100.00	150.00
Palomino	Gloss	—	c.1982	1983	80.00	125.00	175.00
Palomino	Matt	—	c.1982	1983	80.00	125.00	175.00

Model No. 1197

PONY
(Head Up)

Designer: Arthur Gredington
Height: 5 1/2", 14.0 cm

Colourway	Finish	Intro.	Disc.	U.K. £	U.S. $	Can. $
Brown	Gloss	1950	1975	75.00	125.00	175.00
Chestnut	Gloss	1958	1967	150.00	350.00	350.00
Grey	Gloss	1962	1975	95.00	150.00	225.00
Opaque	Gloss	1961	1973	110.00	175.00	225.00
Painted white	Gloss	1961	1967	150.00	350.00	350.00
Palomino	Gloss	1961	1975	80.00	125.00	175.00
Piebald	Gloss	Unknown	Unknown	Extremely Rare		
Rocking horse grey	Gloss	c.1951	1962	175.00	275.00	425.00
White	Matt	1970	1975	100.00	150.00	200.00

Model No. 1261

PALOMINO
(Prancing Arab Type)

Designer: Arthur Gredington
Height: 6 3/4", 17.2 cm

Colourway	Finish	DA #	Intro.	Disc.	U.K. £	U.S. $	Can. $
Brown	Gloss	49	*1961*	1989	65.00	100.00	150.00
Brown	Matt	49	1970	1989	70.00	110.00	165.00
Chestnut	Gloss	—	1958	1967	145.00	225.00	350 00
Grey	Gloss	49	*1961*	1989	75.00	125.00	175.00
Grey	Matt	—	1970	1989	75.00	125.00	175.00
Opaque	Gloss	—	*1961*	1973	95.00	150.00	200.00
Painted white	Gloss	—	*1961*	1967	125.00	200.00	275.00
Palomino	Gloss	49	1952	1989	75.00	125.00	175.00
Palomino	Matt	—	1970	1989	75.00	125.00	175.00
Rocking horse grey	Gloss	—	c.*1956*	1962	165.00	275.00	400.00
White	Matt	—	1970	1982	90.00	150.00	200.00

Model No. 1265   *ARAB "XAYAL"*

The charcoal grey colourway with four white socks is the authentic colouring for "Xayal".

Arab "Xayal"

Arab "Xayal"
Connoisseur Horse

Designer: Arthur Gredington
Height: 6 1/4", 15.9 cm

Colourway	Finish	Intro.	Disc.	U.K. £	U.S. $	Can. $
Brown	Gloss	1952	1989	60.00	100.00	150.00
Charcoal grey	Gloss	1952	1984	85.00	150.00	200.00
Chestnut	Gloss	1958	1967	150.00	250.00	350.00
Grey	Gloss	1961	1989	65.00	100.00	150.00
Opaque	Gloss	1961	1973	95.00	150.00	225.00
Painted white	Gloss	1961	1967	110.00	175.00	250.00
Palomino	Gloss	1961	1989	65.00	100.00	150.00
Rocking horse grey	Gloss	c.1953	1962	175.00	275.00	400.00
White	Matt	1961	1984	70.00	110.00	175.00

SERIES: *Connoisseur Horses*

Height: 7 1/4", 18.4 cm

Colourway	Finish	Intro.	Disc.	U.K. £	U.S. $	Can. $
Dark brown	Matt	1970	1989	95.00	150.00	225.00

Model No. 1359

SUFFOLK PUNCH
"CHAMPION HASSE DAINTY"

Designer: Mr. Orwell
Height: 8", 20.3 cm

Colourway	Finish	Intro.	Disc.	U.K. £	U.S. $	Can. $
Light Chestnut	Gloss	1954	*Unknown*	250.00	400.00	550.00
Dark Chestnut	Gloss	*Unknown*	1971	225.00	350.00	500.00
Grey	Gloss	1965	1965	Extremely Rare		
Palomino	Gloss	Unknown	Unknown	Extremely Rare		

COLOURWAYS DESCRIPTIONS:

Light Chestnut:
Light chestnut horse with much lighter chestnut hooves. Blended thin stripe down the front of the head. Mane and tail are cream with yellow ribbon braided through the mane ending with cream and maroon. Two maroon bows on the tail.

Dark Chestnut:
Much darker chestnut horse with dark chestnust mane and tail. Definite white blaze extending over muzzle, and four short white socks. The mane ribbon is lemon with pink at the end and the tail bows are lemon and pink and indistinct.

Model No. 1361   *HACKNEY*

The black colourway is the authentic colouring of "Black Magic of Nork" and has white patches on the flanks.

Designer: Mr. Orwell
Height: 7 3/4", 19.7 cm

Colourway	Finish	Intro.	Disc.	U.K. £	U.S. $	Can. $
Black	Gloss	1955	1983	95.00	150.00	250.00
Black	Matt	1980	1983	110.00	175.00	265.00
Brown	Gloss	1955	1982	85.00	125.00	200.00
Chestnut	Gloss	1958	1967	200.00	325.00	450.00
Grey	Gloss	*1961*	1975	150.00	250.00	350.00
Opaque	Gloss	*1961*	1973	100.00	150.00	250.00
Painted white	Gloss	*1961*	1967	200.00	325.00	450.00
Palomino	Gloss	*1961*	1970	175.00	275.00	400.00
Rocking horse grey	Gloss	*c.1956*	1962	250.00	400.00	575.00
White	Matt	1970	1982	95.00	150.00	200.00

Model No. 1373   *PINTO PONY*

First Version: Tail is attached to the hind leg from the hock down

Second Verson: Tail hangs loose

Designer: Arthur Gredington
Height: 6 1/2", 16.5 cm

FIRST VERSION: *Tail is attached to the hind leg from the hock down.*

Colourway	Finish	Intro.	Disc.	U.K. £	U.S. $	Can. $
Chestnut	Gloss	1958	1967	175.00	275.00	400.00
Grey	Gloss	1962	1970	Extremely Rare		
Palomino	Gloss	1961	1970	175.00	275.00	400.00
Piebald (black and white)	Gloss	1972	Unknown	95.00	150.00	200.00
Skewbald (brown and white)	Gloss	1955	Unknown	85.00	150.00	200.00

SECOND VERSION: *Tail hangs loose.*

Colourway	Finish	DA #	Intro.	Disc.	U.K. £	U.S. $	Can. $
Piebald (black and white)	Gloss	67	Unknown	1989	75.00	125.00	175.00
Piebald (black and white)	Matt	67	Unknown	1989	75.00	125.00	175.00
Skewbald (brown and white)	Gloss	67	Unknown	1989	75.00	125.00	175.00
Skewbald (brown and white)	Matt	67	Unknown	1989	75.00	125.00	175.00

Model No. 1374   ## GALLOPING HORSE

Model no. 1374 was the horse used for no. 1377 Canadian Mounted Cowboy. However no. 1374 has only three hooves attached to the base compared to four hooves attached in the ridden variety.

Designer: Mr. Orwell
Height: 7 1/2", 19.1 cm

Colourway	Finish	Intro.	Disc.	U.K. £	U.S. $	Can. $
Brown	Gloss	1955	1975	150.00	250.00	375.00
Chestnut	Gloss	1958	1967	225.00	375.00	500.00
Grey	Gloss	1962	1973	175.00	275.00	400.00
Palomino	Gloss	1961	1973	150.00	250.00	375.00

Model No. 1375

CANADIAN MOUNTIE

Designer: Arthur Gredington
Height: 8 1/4", 21.0 cm

Colourway	Finish	Intro.	Disc.	U.K. £	U.S. $	Can. $
Black	Gloss	1955	1976	300.00	500.00	750.00

Model No. 1377

CANADIAN MOUNTED COWBOY

The horse used for model 1377 was also that used for model 1374.

Designer: Mr. Orwell
Height: 8 3/4", 22.2 cm

Colourway	Finish	Intro.	Disc.	U.K. £	U.S. $	Can. $
Palomino	Gloss	1955	1973	380.00	600.00	800.00

Model No. 1391   *MOUNTED INDIAN*

Designer: Mr. Orwell
Height: 8 1/2", 21.6 cm

Colourway	Finish	Intro.	Disc.	U.K. £	U.S. $	Can. $
Skewbald	Gloss	1955	1990	195.00	300.00	450.00

Model No. 1407   *ARAB FOAL*

Designer: Arthur Gredington
Height: 4 1/2", 11.9 cm

Colourway	Finish	DA #	Intro.	Disc.	U.K. £	U.S. $	Can. $
Brown	Gloss	80	1956	1989	30.00	50.00	75.00
Brown	Matt	80	1979	1989	35.00	60.00	80.00
Chestnut	Gloss	—	1958	1967	150.00	250.00	350.00
Grey	Gloss	80	1961	1989	35.00	60.00	80.00
Opaque	Gloss	—	1961	1973	45.00	75.00	100.00
Painted white	Gloss	—	1961	1967	150.00	250.00	350.00
Palomino	Gloss	80	1961	1989	30.00	50.00	75.00
Rocking horse grey	Gloss	—	c.1957	1962	175.00	275.00	400.00
White	Matt	—	1970	1982	50.00	80.00	100.00

Model No. 1480

PONY
(Boy's Pony)

Designer: Arthur Gredington
Height: 3 3/4", 9.5 cm

Colourway	Finish	Intro.	Disc.	U.K. £	U.S. $	Can. $
Brown	Gloss	1957	1967	75.00	125.00	175.00
Chestnut	Gloss	1958	1967	150.00	250.00	350.00
Grey	Gloss	1957	1967	125.00	200.00	275.00
Opaque	Gloss	1957	1967	80.00	125.00	175.00
Painted white	Gloss	1957	1967	125.00	200.00	275.00
Palomino	Gloss	1957	1967	80.00	125.00	175.00
Rocking horse grey	Gloss	1957	1962	175.00	275.00	400.00

Model No. 1483

PONY
(Girl's Pony)

Designer: Arthur Gredington
Height: 5", 12.7 cm

Colourway	Finish	Intro.	Disc.	U.K. £	U.S. $	Can. $
Brown	Gloss	1957	1967	75.00	125.00	175.00
Chestnut	Gloss	1958	1967	150.00	250.00	350.00
Grey	Gloss	1957	1967	125.00	200.00	275.00
Opaque	Gloss	1957	1967	80.00	125.00	175.00
Painted white	Gloss	1957	1967	125.00	200.00	275.00
Palomino	Gloss	1957	1967	80.00	125.00	175.00
Rocking horse grey	Gloss	1957	1962	175.00	275.00	400.00
Skewbald (brown and white)	Gloss	1957	1967	85.00	135.00	200.00

Model No. 1484

HUNTSMAN'S HORSE

This model was used as the horse in model no. 1501 "The Huntsman".

Designer: Arthur Gredington
Height: 6 3/4", 17.2 cm

Colourway	Finish	Intro.	Disc.	U.K. £	U.S. $	Can. $
Brown	Gloss	1957	1982	60.00	95.00	150.00
Chestnut	Gloss	1958	1967	150.00	250.00	350.00
Grey	Gloss	1957	1982	65.00	100.00	150.00
Opaque	Gloss	1957	1973	80.00	125.00	200.00
Painted white	Gloss	1957	1967	125.00	200.00	275.00
Palomino	Gloss	1957	1982	60.00	95.00	150.00
Rocking horse grey	Gloss	1957	1962	175.00	300.00	400.00
White	Matt	1970	1982	70.00	125.00	175.00

Model No. 1499   *GIRL ON PONY*

The pony used for model no. 1499 was also available separately as model no. 1483 "Girl's Pony".

Designer: Arthur Gredington
Height: 5 1/2", 14.0 cm

Colourway	Finish	Intro.	Disc.	U.K. £	U.S. $	Can. $
Brown	Gloss	1957	1965			
Light dapple grey	Gloss	c.1961	1965	Extremely Rare		
Rocking horse grey	Gloss	c.1961	1962			
Skewbald	Gloss	1957	1965	110.00	200.00	300.00

Model No. 1500

BOY ON PONY

The pony used for model number 1500 was also available separately as model number 1480 "Boy's Pony".

Designer: Arthur Gredington
Height: 5 1/2", 14.0 cm

Colourway	Finish	Intro.	Disc.	U.K. £	U.S. $	Can. $
Brown	Gloss	c.1961	1976	Extremely Rare		
Light dapple grey	Gloss	c.1961	1976	Extremely Rare		
Palomino	Gloss	1957	1976	110.00	200.00	300.00
Rocking horse grey	Gloss	c.1961	1962	Extremely Rare		

Model No. 1501   *HUNTSMAN*

STYLE TWO: *Standing*

Designer: Arthur Gredington
Height: 8 1/4", 21.0 cm

Colourway	Finish	Intro.	Disc.	U.K. £	U.S. $	Can. $
Brown	Gloss	1957	1995	100.00	150.00	250.00
Chestnut	Gloss	1965	1967	300.00	475.00	675.00
Grey	Gloss	1962	1975	175.00	300.00	425.00
Opaque	Gloss	1971	1973	175.00	300.00	425.00
Painted white	Gloss	1958	1971	250.00	400.00	575.00
Palomino	Gloss	1965	1971	275.00	450.00	650.00
Rocking horse grey	Gloss	c.1958	1962	Extremely Rare		
White	Matt	1971	1981	150.00	250.00	350.00

Model No. 1516

APPALOOSA
(Spotted Walking Pony)

Designer: Arthur Gredington
Height: 5 1/4", 13.3 cm

Colourway	Finish	Intro.	Disc.	U.K. £	U.S. $	Can. $
Brown	Gloss	*1958*	*1967*	175.00	300.00	400.00
Chestnut	Gloss	*1958*	1967	200.00	325.00	450.00
Grey	Gloss	*1958*	1967	175.00	300.00	400.00
Opaque	Gloss	*1958*	1967	125.00	225.00	300.00
Painted white	Gloss	*1958*	1967	200.00	325.00	450.00
Palomino	Gloss	*1958*	1967	175.00	300.00	400.00
Rocking horse grey	Gloss	*1958*	1962	275.00	475.00	650.00
Spotted (British)	Gloss	1957	1966	200.00	325.00	450.00

Model No. 1546

H.M. QUEEN ELIZABETH II
ON IMPERIAL

The horse "Imperial" was also available separately as model number 1557.

Designer: Mr. Folkard
Height: 10 1/2", 26.7 cm

Colourway	Finish	Intro.	Disc.	U.K. £	U.S. $	Can. $
Chestnut	Gloss	1958	1981	225.00	375.00	550.00

Model No. 1549

HORSE
(Head Tucked, Leg Up)

Designer: Pal Zalmen
Height: 7 1/2", 19.1 cm

Colourway	Finish	DA #	Intro.	Disc.	U.K. £	U.S. $	Can. $
Brown	Gloss	51	1958	1989	65.00	120.00	175.00
Chestnut	Gloss	—	1958	1967	125.00	200.00	300.00
Grey	Gloss	—	*1961*	1989	65.00	120.00	175.00
Grey	Matt	—	1981	1989	70.00	120.00	175.00
Opaque	Gloss	—	1964	1973	110.00	175.00	275.00
Painted white	Gloss	—	*1961*	1967	150.00	250.00	350.00
Palomino	Gloss	—	*1961*	1989	65.00	120.00	175.00
Palomino	Matt	—	1981	1989	70.00	120.00	175.00
Rocking horse grey	Gloss	—	*c.1959*	*1962*	175.00	300.00	400.00
White	Matt	—	1970	1982	90.00	150.00	225.00

Model No. 1557   *"IMPERIAL"*

This horse was used in model no. 1546 with Queen Elizabeth as rider.

Designer: Mr. Hayward and Albert Hallam
Height: 8 1/4", 21.0 cm

Colourway	Finish	Intro.	Disc.	U.K. £	U.S. $	Can. $
Brown	Gloss	1958	1982	85.00	135.00	200.00
Chestnut	Gloss	1958	1967	125.00	200.00	350.00
Grey	Gloss	1958	1982	85.00	135.00	200.00
Opaque	Gloss	1958	1973	95.00	150.00	225.00
Painted white	Gloss	1958	1967	150.00	250.00	350.00
Palomino	Gloss	1958	1982	85.00	135.00	200.00
Rocking horse grey	Gloss	1958	1962	175.00	300.00	400.00
White	Matt	1970	1982	95.00	150.00	225.00

Model No. 1564   *LARGE RACEHORSE*

This is the underlying model for the Connoisseur horse 1564 and the Harnessed version 1564.

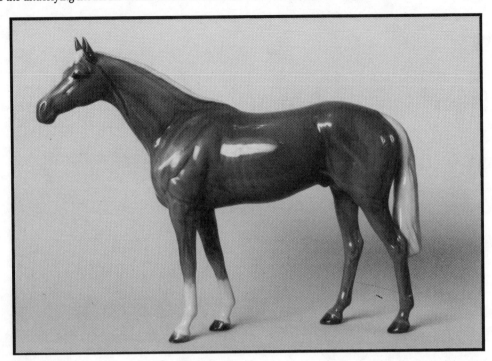

Designer: Arthur Gredington
Height: 11 1/4", 28.5 cm

Colourway	Finish	Intro.	Disc.	U.K. £	U.S. $	Can. $
Brown	Gloss	1959	1982	150.00	250.00	350.00
Chestnut	Gloss	1959	1967	275.00	450.00	600.00
Grey	Gloss	1959	1982	165.00	265.00	375.00
Opaque	Gloss	1959	1973	185.00	300.00	400.00
Painted white	Gloss	1959	1967	175.00	275.00	400.00
Palomino	Gloss	1959	1982	165.00	265.00	375.00
Rocking horse grey	Gloss	1959	1962	350.00	575.00	775.00
White	Matt	1970	1982	175.00	275.00	400.00

SERIES: *Connoisseur Horse*

Designer: Arthur Gredington
Height: 12 1/4", 31.1 cm

Colourway	Finish	Intro.	Disc.	U.K. £	U.S. $	Can. $
Brown	Matt	1970	1981	200.00	300.00	450.00

SERIES: *Harnessed Horses*

Height: 11 1/4", 28.5 cm

Colourway	Finish	Intro.	Disc.	U.K. £	U.S. $	Can. $
Brown	Gloss	1974	By 1981	250.00	400.00	575.00

Model No. 1588

H.R.H. DUKE OF EDINBURGH
ON ALAMEIN

Designer: Mr. Folkard
Height: 10 1/2', 26.7 cm

Colourway	Finish	Intro.	Disc.	U.K. £	U.S. $	Can. $
Light dapple grey	Gloss	1958	1981	225.00	375.00	525.00

Model No. 1624

LIFEGUARD

STYLE ONE: *With trumpet*

Designer: Arthur Gredington
Height: 9 1/2", 24.0 cm

Colourway	Finish	DA #	Intro.	Disc.	U.K. £	U.S. $	Can. $
Light dapple grey	Gloss	22	1959	1977	350.00	550.00	775.00

Model No. 1641

CONNEMARA PONY
"TERESE OF LEAM"

SERIES: Mountain and Moorland Ponies.

Designer: Arthur Gredington
Height: 7", 17.8 cm

Colourway	Finish	Intro.	Disc.	U.K. £	U.S. $	Can. $
Grey	Gloss	1961	1984	110.00	175.00	275.00

Model No. 1642

DARTMOOR PONY
"JENTYL"

SERIES: *Mountain and Moorland Ponies.*

Designer: Arthur Gredington
Height: 6 1/4", 15.9 cm

Colourway	Finish	Intro.	Disc.	U.K. £	U.S. $	Can. $
Bay	Gloss	1961	1984	100.00	150.00	200.00

Model No. 1643

WELSH MOUNTAIN PONY
"COED COCH MADOG"

SERIES: *Mountain and Moorland Ponies.*

First Version: Tail is attached to off-side hind leg   Second Version: Tail hangs loose

Designer: Arthur Gredington
Height: 6 1/4", 15.9 cm

FIRST VERSION: *Tail is attached to off-side hind leg.*

Colourway	Finish	Intro.	Disc.	U.K. £	U.S. $	Can. $
Grey	Gloss	1961	Unknown	125.00	200.00	300.00

SECOND VERSION: *Tail hangs loose*

Colourway	Finish	Intro.	Disc.	U.K. £	U.S. $	Can. $
Grey	Gloss	Unknown	1989	110.00	175.00	250.00

Model No. 1644

HIGHLAND PONY
"MACKIONNEACH"

SERIES: *Mountain and Moorland Ponies.*

Designer: Arthur Gredington
Height: 7 1/4", 18.4 cm

Colourway	Finish	Intro.	Disc.	U.K. £	U.S. $	Can. $
Dun	Gloss	1961	1989	100.00	150.00	200.00
Opaque	Gloss	Unknown	Unknown	Extremely Rare		

Model No. 1645

EXMOOR PONY
"HEATHERMAN"

SERIES: *Mountain and Moorland Ponies.*

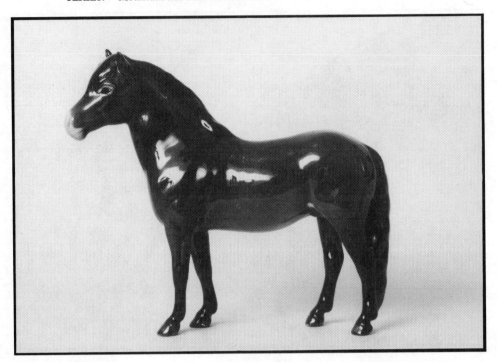

Designer: Arthur Gredington
Height: 6 1/2", 16.5 cm

Colourway	Finish	Intro.	Disc.	U.K. £	U.S. $	Can. $
Bay	Gloss	1961	1983	110.00	200.00	275.00

Model No. 1646

NEW FOREST PONY
"JONATHEN 3RD"

SERIES: *Mountain and Moorland Ponies.*

First Version: Tail is attached to the near-side hock

Second Verson: Tail hangs loose

Designer: Arthur Gredington
Height: 7", 17.8 cm

FIRST VERSION: *Tail is attached to the near-side hock.*

Colourway	Finish	Intro.	Disc.	U.K. £	U.S. $	Can. $
Bay	Gloss	1961	Unknown	125.00	200.00	300.00

SECOND VERSION: *Tail hangs loose.*

Colourway	Finish	Intro.	Disc.	U.K. £	U.S. $	Can. $
Bay	Gloss	Unknown	1984	110.00	200.00	275.00

Model No. 1647

FELL PONY
"DENE DAUNTLESS"

SERIES: *Mountain and Moorland Ponies.*

Designer: Arthur Gredington
Height: 6 3/4"

Colourway	Finish	Intro.	Disc.	U.K. £	U.S. $	Can. $
Black	Gloss	1961	1982	100.00	150.00	225.00

Model No. 1648

SHETLAND PONY
"ESCHONCHAN RONAY"

SERIES: Mountain and Moorland Ponies.

Designer: Arthur Gredington
Height: 4 3/4", 12.1 cm

Colourway	Finish	Intro.	Disc.	U.K. £	U.S. $	Can. $
Brown	Gloss	1961	1989	75.00	125.00	175.00

Model No. 1671

DALES PONY
"MAISIE"

SERIES: **Mountain and Moorland Ponies.**

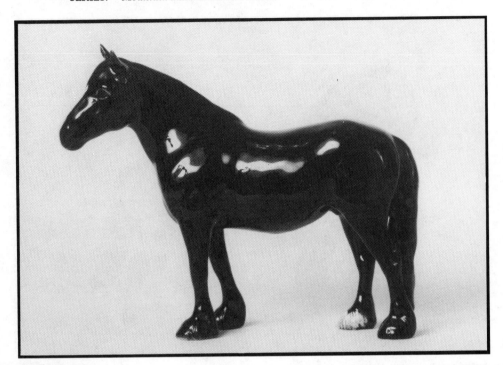

Designer: Arthur Gredington
Height: 6 1/2", 16.5 cm

Colourway	Finish	Intro.	Disc.	U.K. £	U.S. $	Can. $
Black	Gloss	1961	1982	95.00	175.00	250.00

Model No. 1730

HUNTSWOMAN

STYLE TWO:

Designer: Arthur Gredington
Height: 8 1/4", 21.0 cm

Colourway	Finish	Intro.	Disc.	U.K. £	U.S. $	Can. $
Brown	Gloss	1960	1975	175.00	275.00	400.00
Grey	Gloss	1960	1995	110.00	175.00	250.00
Opaque	Gloss	1971	1973	225.00	375.00	500.00
Painted white	Gloss	1960	1971	Extremely Rare		
Rocking horse grey	Gloss	1960	1962	Extremely Rare		
White	Matt	1971	1981	175.00	275.00	400.00

Model No. 1734

LARGE HUNTER

FIRST VERSION: *The head looks slightly overlarge and the body too much on the thin size. The tail hangs straight down.*

Designer: Arthur Gredington
Height: 11 1/4", 28.5 cm

Colourway	Finish	Intro.	Disc.	U.K. £	U.S. $	Can. $
Brown	Gloss	1961	1963			
Chestnut	Gloss	1961	1963			
Grey	Gloss	1961	1963			
Opaque	Gloss	1961	1963		Extremely Rare	
Painted white	Gloss	1961	1963			
Palomino	Gloss	1961	1963			
Rocking horse grey	Gloss	1961	1962			

Second Version: Large Hunter
Head and body in proportion, tail is
slightly arched away from the body

Large Hunter
Connoisseur Horse

SECOND VERSION: *Head and boby in proportion. The tail is slightly arched away from the body.*

Height: 11 3/4", 29.8 cm

Colourway	Finish	Intro.	Disc.	U.K. £	U.S. $	Can. $
Brown	Gloss	1963	1984	125.00	200.00	300.00
Chestnut	Gloss	1963	1967	225.00	350.00	500.00
Grey	Gloss	1963	1984	125.00	200.00	300.00
Opaque	Gloss	1963	1973	175.00	275.00	400.00
Painted white	Gloss	1963	1967	225.00	350.00	500.00
Palomino	Gloss	1963	1983	150.00	250.00	350.00
White	Matt	1970	1982	195.00	300.00	450.00

SERIES: *Connoisseur Horses*

Height: 12 1/4", 31.1 cm

Colourway	Finish	Intro.	Disc.	U.K. £	U.S. $	Can. $
Grey	Matt	1970	1982	150.00	250.00	350.00

Model No. 1771

ARAB "BAHRAM"

Designer: Arthur Gredington
Height: 7 1/2", 19.1 cm

Colourway	Finish	DA #	Intro.	Disc.	U.K. £	U.S. $	Can. $
Brown	Gloss	52	1961	1989	50.00	80.00	125.00
Brown	Matt	52	1980	1989	55.00	90.00	125.00
Chestnut	Gloss	—	1961	1967	150.00	250.00	350.00
Grey	Gloss	—	1961	1989	75.00	125.00	175.00
Grey	Matt	—	1980	1989	85.00	135.00	200.00
Opaque	Gloss	—	1961	1973	110.00	175.00	250.00
Painted white	Gloss	—	1961	1967	175.00	300.00	400.00
Palomino	Gloss	—	1961	1989	65.00	100.00	150.00
Palomino	Matt	—	1980	1989	75.00	125.00	175.00
Rocking horse grey	Gloss	—	1961	1962	Extremely Rare		
White	Matt	—	1970	1982	95.00	150.00	225.00

SERIES: *Connoisseur Horses*

Height: 8 1/4", 21.0 cm

Colourway	Finish	Intro.	Disc.	U.K. £	U.S. $	Can. $
Grey	Matt	1970	1989	95.00	175.00	250.00

Model No. 1772　　　　*THOROUGHBRED STALLION - LARGE*

Thoroughbred Stallion

Thoroughbred Stallion
Connoisseur Horse

Designer: Arthur Gredington
Height:　8", 20.3 cm

Colourway	Finish	DA #	Intro.	Disc.	U.K. £	U.S. $	Can. $
Brown	Gloss	53	1961	1989	50.00	85.00	115.00
Chestnut	Gloss	—	1961	1967	175.00	275.00	400.00
Grey	Gloss	53	1961	1989	65.00	100.00	150.00
Opaque	Gloss	—	1961	1973	115.00	185.00	275.00
Painted white	Gloss	—	1961	1967	175.00	275.00	400.00
Palomino	Gloss	—	1961	1983	85.00	150.00	200.00
Rocking horse grey	Gloss	—	1961	1962	Extremely Rare		
White	Matt	—	1970	1982	75.00	130.00	175.00

SERIES:　*Connoisseur Horses*

Height:　8 3/4", 22.2 cm

Colourway	Finish	Intro.	Disc.	U.K. £	U.S. $	Can. $
Bay	Matt	1970	1989	90.00	150.00	225.00

Model No. 1772A

APPALOOSA STALLION

COLOURWAY No. 1:   *More detailed paintwork with the head and neck in particular more "mottled" Striped hooves.*

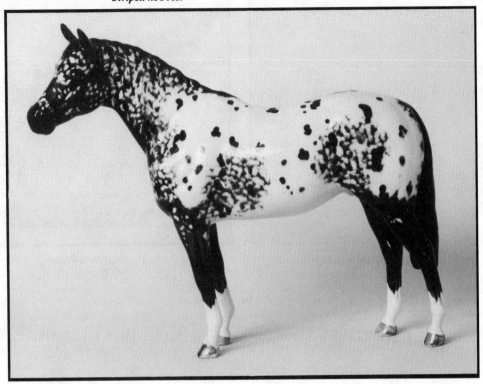

Designer: Arthur Gredington
Height: 8", 20.3 cm

Colourway	Finish	Intro.	Disc.	U.K. £	U.S. $	Can. $
Black and white	Gloss	1975	Unknown	95.00	150.00	225.00

COLOURWAY No.2:   *Less distinct roan areas of black on head and neck and brown on lower body quarters. Cream hooves.*

Colourway	Finish	Intro.	Disc.	U.K. £	U.S. $	Can. $
Black and white	Gloss	Unknown	1989	75.00	125.00	175.00

Model No. 1793

WELSH COB
(Standing)

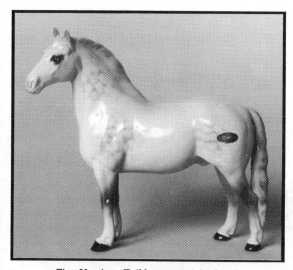

First Version: Tail hangs straight down

Second Version: The top part of the tail (dock)
arched away from the body

Designer: Arthur Gredington
Height: 7 1/2", 19.1 cm

FIRST VERSION: *Tail hangs straight down*

Colourway	Finish	Intro.	Disc.	U.K. £	U.S. $	Can. $
Brown	Gloss	1962	c.1975/76	85.00	150.00	225.00
Chestnut	Gloss	1962	c.1975/76	150.00	225.00	350.00
Grey	Gloss	1962	c.1975/76	95.00	150.00	225.00
Opaque	Gloss	1962	c.1975/76	110.00	175.00	275.00
Painted white	Gloss	1962	c.1975/76	175.00	300.00	400.00
Palomino	Gloss	1962	1970	150.00	225.00	350.00
Piebald	Gloss	Unknown	Unknown	Extremely Rare		
White	Matt	1970	c.1975/76	110.00	175.00	275.00

SECOND VERSION: *The tail was altered so that the top part (dock) arched away from the body.*

Colourway	Finish	Intro.	Disc.	U.K. £	U.S. $	Can. $
Brown	Gloss	c.1975/76	1982	75.00	125.00	175.00
Grey	Gloss	c.1975/76	1982	85.00	150.00	225.00
White	Matt	c.1975/76	1982	85.00	150.00	225.00

Model No. 1811   *MARE AND FOAL*

The mare and foal are available separately as model nos. 1812 mare and 1813 foal.

Designer: Arthur Gredington
Height: 6", 15.0 cm

Colourway	Finish	Intro.	Disc.	U.K. £	U.S. $	Can. $
Brown mare and chestnut foal	Gloss	1962	1975	125.00	225.00	350.00
Grey mare and black foal	Gloss	1962	1975	145.00	275.00	400.00

Model No. 1812

MARE
(Facing Right, Head Down)

Model no. 1811 was paired with foal model no. 1813 to make model no. 1811 "Mare and Foal".

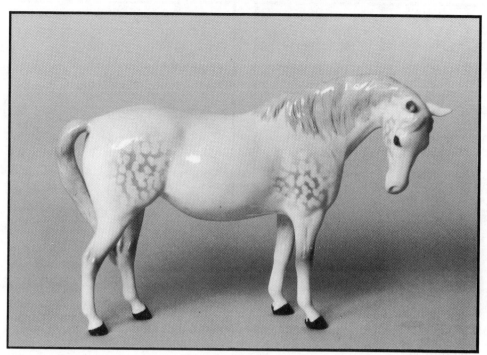

Designer: Arthur Gredington
Height: 5 3/4", 14.6 cm

Colourway	Finish	DA #	Intro.	Disc.	U.K. £	U.S. $	Can. $
Brown	Gloss	54	1962	1989	55.00	100.00	150.00
Brown	Matt	—	1970	1989	55.00	100.00	150.00
Chestnut	Gloss	—	1962	1967	150.00	275.00	375.00
Grey	Gloss	—	1962	1989	55.00	100.00	150.00
Grey	Matt	—	1970	1989	55.00	100.00	150.00
Opaque	Gloss	—	1962	1973	95.00	175.00	250.00
Painted white	Gloss	—	1962	1967	125.00	200.00	300.00
Palomino	Gloss	—	1962	1989	55.00	100.00	150.00
Palomino	Matt	—	1970	1983	85.00	150.00	200.00
"Treacle"	Gloss	—	1992	1992	75.00	125.00	175.00
"Treacle"	Matt	—	1992	1992	75.00	125.00	175.00
White	Matt	—	1970	1982	100.00	175.00	200.00

Model No. 1813

FOAL
(Larger Thoroughbred Type)

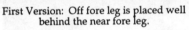

First Version: Off fore leg is placed well behind the near fore leg.

Second Version: Off fore leg almost parallel to near fore leg

Designer: Arthur Gredington
Height: 4 1/2", 11.9 cm

FIRST VERSION: *Fine head and legs, off fore leg is placed well behind the near fore leg.*

Colourway	Finish	Intro.	Disc.	U.K. £	U.S. $	Can. $
Brown	Gloss	1962	1982	35.00	60.00	95.00
Brown	Matt	1979	1982	35.00	60.00	95.00
Chestnut	Gloss	1962	1967	130.00	225.00	300.00
Grey	Gloss	1962	1982	50.00	95.00	125.00
Opaque	Gloss	1962	1973	65.00	110.00	150.00
Painted white	Gloss	1963	1967	130.00	225.00	300.00
Palomino	Gloss	1962	1982	35.00	60.00	95.00
White	Matt	1970	1982	50.00	95.00	125.00

SECOND VERSION: *Plain head, thicker legs with less shape, off fore leg almost parallel to near fore leg.*

Colourway	Finish	DA #	Intro.	Disc.	U.K. £	U.S. $	Can. $
Brown	Gloss	81	1982	1982	75.00	125.00	175.00
Brown	Matt	81	1982	1989	35.00	60.00	95.00
Grey	Gloss	—	1982	1989	35.00	60.00	95.00
Palomino	Gloss	—	1982	1989	35.00	60.00	95.00
Orange Bay	Gloss	—	1982	c.1984	100.00	175.00	250.00

Model No. 1816

FOAL
(Smaller Thoroughbred Type, Facing Left)

First Version: Fine head, thin delicate legs

Second Version: Head and legs thicker

Designer: Arthur Gredington
Height: 3 1/2", 8.9 cm

FIRST VERSON: *Fine head and very thin delicate legs.*

Colourway	Finish	Intro.	Disc.	U.K. £	U.S. $	Can. $
Brown	Gloss	1963	1975	45.00	75.00	100.00
Chestnut	Gloss	1963	1967	150.00	250.00	350.00
Grey	Gloss	1963	1975	65.00	100.00	150.00
Opaque	Gloss	1963	1973	85.00	150.00	200.00
Painted white	Gloss	1963	1967	150.00	250.00	350.00
Palomino	Gloss	1963	1975	45.00	75.00	100.00
White	Matt	1970	1975	65.00	100.00	150.00

SECOND VERSON: *Head and legs made thicker and less shape to the legs.*

Colourway	Finish	Intro.	Disc.	U.K. £	U.S. $	Can. $
Brown	Gloss	1975	1989	35.00	55.00	85.00
Brown	Matt	1979	1989	35.00	55.00	85.00
Grey	Gloss	1975	1983	50.00	75.00	110.00
Palomino	Gloss	1975	1989	40.00	65.00	90.00
White	Matt	1975	1989	40.00	65.00	90.00

Model No. 1817

FOAL
(Smaller Thoroughbred Type, Facing Right)

Designer: Arthur Gredington
Height: 3 1/4", 8.3 cm

Colourway	Finish	Intro.	Disc.	U.K. £	U.S. $	Can. $
Brown	Gloss	1963	1975	45.00	70.00	100.00
Chestnut	Gloss	1963	1967	130.00	200.00	300.00
Grey	Gloss	1963	1975	45.00	70.00	100.00
Opaque	Gloss	1963	1973	65.00	100.00	150.00
Painted white	Gloss	1963	1967	130.00	200.00	300.00
Palomino	Gloss	1963	1975	60.00	95.00	135.00
White	Matt	1970	1975	60.00	95.00	135.00

Model No. 1862

HORSE AND JOCKEY

STYLE TWO: *"Standing" horse and jockey*

Designer: Arthur Gredington
Height: 8", 20.3 cm

Colourway	Finish	Intro.	Disc.	U.K. £	U.S. $	Can. $
Brown	Gloss	1963	1984	250.00	425.00	575.00
Light dapple grey	Gloss	1963	1983	275.00	475.00	650.00

Model No. 1991

MARE
(Facing Right, Head Up)

FIRST VERSION: *The end only of the tail is attached to the hock.*

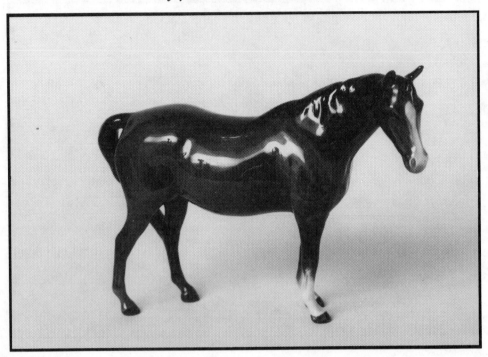

Designer: Arthur Gredington
Height: 5 1/2", 14.0 cm

Colourway	Finish	DA #	Intro.	Disc.	U.K. £	U.S. $	Can. $
Brown	Gloss	55	1965	Unknown	65.00	110.00	175.00
Brown	Matt	55	1970	Unknown	65.00	110.00	175.00
Chestnut	Gloss	—	1965	Unknown	185.00	325.00	450.00
Grey	Gloss	55	1965	Unknown	65.00	110.00	175.00
Grey	Matt	—	1970	Unknown	65.00	110.00	175.00
Opaque	Gloss	—	1965	Unknown	110.00	200.00	275.00
Painted white	Gloss	—	1965	Unknown	120.00	225.00	300.00
Palomino	Gloss	55	1965	Unknown	65.00	110.00	175.00
Palomino	Matt	—	1970	Unknown	65.00	110.00	175.00
White	Matt	—	1970	Unknown	85.00	135.00	200.00

SECOND VERSION: *The tail is attached to the quarters and the hock.*

Colourway	Finish	DA #	Intro.	Disc.	U.K. £	U.S. $	Can. $
Brown	Gloss	55	Unknown	1989	65.00	110.00	175.00
Brown	Matt	55	Unknown	1989	65.00	110.00	175.00
Chestnut	Gloss	—	Unknown	1967	185.00	325.00	450.00
Grey	Gloss	55	Unknown	1989	65.00	110.00	175.00
Grey	Matt	—	Unknown	1989	65.00	110.00	175.00
Opaque	Gloss	—	Unknown	1973	110.00	200.00	275.00
Painted white	Gloss	—	Unknown	1967	120.00	225.00	300.00
Palomino	Gloss	55	Unknown	1989	65.00	110.00	175.00
Palomino	Matt	—	Unknown	1989	65.00	110.00	175.00
White	Matt	—	Unknown	1982	85.00	135.00	200.00

Model No. 1992

THOROUGHBRED STALLION
(Small)

Designer: Arthur Gredington
Height: 5 1/2", 14.0.cm

Colourway	Finish	DA #	Intro.	Disc.	U.K. £	U.S. $	Can. $
Brown	Gloss	56	1965	1989	65.00	100.00	150.00
Brown	Matt	56	1970	1989	65.00	100.00	150.00
Chestnut	Gloss	—	1965	1967	175.00	300.00	425.00
Grey	Gloss	56	1965	1989	75.00	125.00	175.00
Grey	Matt	—	1970	1989	75.00	125.00	175.00
Opaque	Gloss	—	1965	1973	85.00	150.00	200.00
Painted white	Gloss	—	1965	1967	125.00	225.00	300.00
Palomino	Gloss	—	1965	1989	85.00	150.00	200.00
Palomino	Matt	—	1970	1989	65.00	100.00	150.00
White	Matt	—	1970	1982	75.00	125.00	175.00

Model No. 2065

ARKLE

SERIES: *Connoisseur Horses*

Designer: Arthur Gredington
Height: 11 7/8"

Colourway	Finish	DA #	Intro.	Disc.	U.K. £	U.S. $	Can. $
Bay	Matt	15	1970	1989	175.00	300.00	425.00

Model No. 2084

ARKLE
PAT TAAFFE UP

SERIES: *Connoisseur Horses*

Designer: Arthur Gredington
Height: 12 1/2", 21.7 cm

Colourway	Finish	Intro.	Disc.	U.K. £	U.S. $	Can. $
Bay	Matt	1970	1982	295.00	500.00	675.00

Model No. 2186

QUARTER HORSE

Designer: Arthur Gredington
Height: 8 1/4", 21.0 cm

Colourway	Finish	Intro.	Disc.	U.K. £	U.S. $	Can. $
Brown	Gloss	1969	1982	110.00	200.00	275.00
Brown	Matt	1970	1982	110.00	200.00	275.00
White	Matt	1973	1982	100.00	175.00	250.00

Model No. 2210

HIGHWAYMAN

SERIES: *Connoisseur Horses*

Designer: Albert Hallam
Height: 13 3/4", 34.9 cm

Colourway	Finish	Intro.	Disc.	U.K. £	U.S. $	Can. $
Bay	Matt	1970	1975	650.00	1,000.00	1,400.00

Model No. 2242

ARAB STALLION

This is an authentic rendition of an Arab horse. It is on a pottery (base) stand.

Designer: Albert Hallam
Height: 8 1/2", 21.6 cm

Colourway	Finish	Intro.	Disc.	U.K. £	U.S. $	Can. $
Brown	Gloss	1970	1975	350.00	575.00	800.00

Model No. 2269

ARAB STALLION WITH SADDLE

SERIES: *Connoisseur Horses*

Designer: Albert Hallam
Height: 9 1/2", 24.0 cm

Colourway	Finish	Intro.	Disc.	U.K. £	U.S. $	Can.
2269	Matt	1970	1975	450.00	700.00	1,000.00

Model No. 2275

BEDOUIN ARAB

SERIES *Connoisseur Horses*

Designer: Albert Hallam
Height: 11 1/2", 29.2 cm

Colourway	Finish	Intro.	Disc.	U.K. £	U.S. $	Can. $
Chestnut	Matt	1970	1975	775.00	1,200.00	1,500.00

Model No. 2282

NORWEGIAN FJORD HORSE

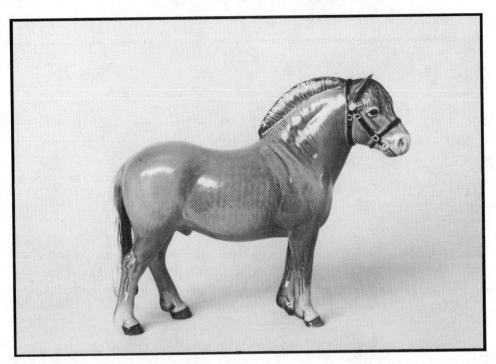

Designer: Albert Hallan
Height: 6 1/2", 16.5 cm

Colourway	Finish	Intro.	Disc.	U.K. £	U.S. $	Can. $
Dun	Gloss	1970	1975	350.00	550.00	775.00

Model No. 2309

BURNHAM BEAUTY

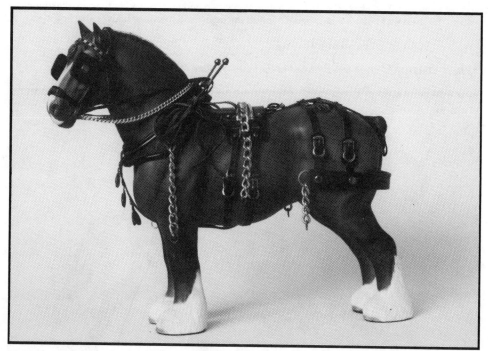

Designer: Albert Hallam
Height: 10 3/4", 27.8 cm

Colourway	Finish	Intro.	Disc.	U.K. £	U.S. $	Can. $
Brown	Gloss	1972	1982	150.00	250.00	350.00
White	Matt	1974	1982	175.00	300.00	400.00

SERIES: *Connoisseur Horses*

Height: 11 1/4", 28.5 cm

Colourway	Finish	Intro.	Disc.	U.K. £	U.S. $	Can. $
Bay	Matt	1971	1982	150.00	250.00	350.00

SERIES: *Harnessed Horses*

Height: 10 3/4", 27.8 cm

Colourway	Finish	Intro.	Disc.	U.K. £	U.S. $	Can. $
Brown	Matt	1979	1984	175.00	300.00	400.00

Model No. 2340

CARDIGAN BAY

Two versions of model no. 2340 exist. The first version has only two hooves attached to the base making it unstable and prone to breakage. The base was remodelled to better support the model and has three hooves attached to it.

SERIES: *Connoisseur Horses*

FIRST VERSION: *Two legs attached to the base - off hind leg is not attached to the base.*

Designer: Albert Hallam
Height: 9 1/4", 23.5 cm

Colourway	Finish	Intro.	Disc.	U.K. £	U.S. $	Can. $
Brown	Matt	1971	c.1972	500.00	900.00	1,250.00

SECOND VERSION: *Three legs attached to the base - off hind leg is attached to the base.*

Colourway	Finish	Intro.	Disc.	U.K. £	U.S. $	Can. $
Brown	Matt	c.1972	1976	350.00	600.00	800.00

Model No. 2345

NIJINSKY

SERIES: *Connoisseur Horses*

Designer: Albert Hallam
Height: 11 1/4", 28.5 cm

Colourway	Finsh	DA #	Intro.	Disc.	U.K. £	U.S. $	Can. $
Bay	Matt	16	1971	1989	175.00	300.00	425.00

Model No. 2352

NIJINSKY
LESTER PIGGOTT UP

SERIES: **Connoisseur Horses**

Designer: Albert Hallam
Height: 12 1/2", 31.7 cm

Colourway	Finish	Intro.	Disc.	U.K. £	U.S. $	Can. $
Bay	Matt	1971	1982	295.00	500.00	675.00

Model No. 2421

THE WINNER

Designer: Albert Hallam
Height: 9 1/2", 24.0 cm

Colourway	Finish	Intro.	Disc.	U.K. £	U.S. $	Can. $
Brown	Gloss	1973	1982	125.00	200.00	300.00
Brown	Matt	1973	1982	110.00	175.00	275.00
White	Matt	1973	1982	125.00	200.00	300.00

Model No. 2422   *MILL REEF*

The mahogany bay (gloss) variety was sold through Lawleys, Royal Doulton's retail shops, in the mid 1980s. When "Mill Reef" was withdrawn from the range at the end of 1989 a white matt variety was sold at the Beswick factory shop.

Designer: Albert Hallam
Height: Height: 9", 22.9 cm

Colourway	Finish	Intro.	Disc.	U.K. £	U.S. $	Can. $
Mahogany Bay	Gloss	1985	1988	120.00	200.00	325.00
White	Matt	1989	Unknown	145.00	250.00	350.00

SERIES: *Connoisseur Horses*

Colourway	Finish	Intro.	Disc.	U.K. £	U.S. $	Can. $
Brown/wooden plinth	Matt	1973	1989	145.00	250.00	350.00

Model No. 2431

MOUNTIE STALLION

SERIES: *Connoisseur*

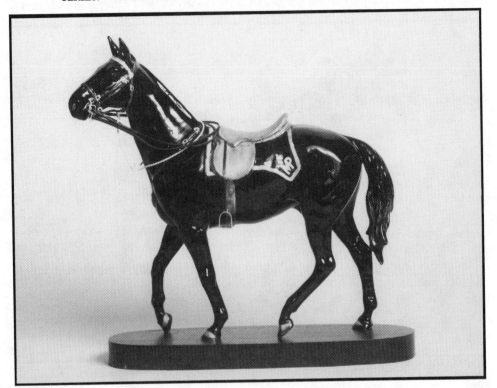

Designer: Graham Tongue
Height: 10", 25.4 cm

Colourway	Finish	Intro.	Disc.	U.K. £	U.S. $	Can. $
Black	Gloss	1973	1975	450.00	750.00	1,000.00

Model No. 2459

SHIRE MARE
(Lying)

Designer: Royal Doulton
Height: 5", 12.7 cm

Colourways	Finish	Intro.	Disc.	U.K. £	U.S. $	Can. $
Brown	Gloss	1973	Unknown	200.00	325.00	450.00
Grey	Gloss	1973	1976	175.00	300.00	400.00

Model No. 2460

SHIRE FOAL
(Lying)

Designer: Royal Doulton
Height: 3 1/2", 8.9 cm

Colourway	Finish	Intro.	Disc.	U.K. £	U.S. $	Can. $
Dark Brown	Gloss	1973	1976	145.00	225.00	325.00

Model No. 2464   *PERCHERON*

SERIES: *Harnessed Horses*

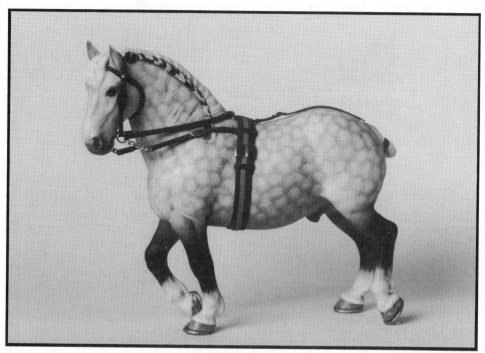

Designer: Unknown
Height: 9 3/4", 24.7 cm

Colourway	Finish	Intro.	Disc.	U.K. £	U.S. $	Can. $
Dappled grey	Matt	1974	1982	275.00	450.00	600.00

Model No. 2465

CLYDESDALE

SERIES: *Harnessed Horses*

Designer: Unknown
Height: 10 3/4", 27.8 cm

FIRST VERSION: *Working Harness*

Colourway	Finish	Intro.	Disc.	U.K. £	U.S. $	Can. $
Chocolate Brown	Matt	1974	1982	175.00	275.00	400.00

SECOND VERSION: *Show Harness*

Colourway	Finish	Intro.	Disc.	U.K. £	U.S. $	Can. $
Chocolate Brown	Matt	1974	1982	175.00	275.00	400.00

Model No. 2466

BLACK BEAUTY

This model was used in model # 2466/2536 Black Beauty and Foal.

Designer: Graham Tongue
Height: 7 1/4", 18.4 cm

Colourway	Finish	DA #	Intro.	Disc.	U.K. £	U.S. $	Can. $
Black	Matt	65	1974	1989	75.00	125.00	175.00

Model No. 2467   LIPIZZANER WITH RIDER

SERIES: *Connoisseur Horses*

First Version: Hind legs attached to
a circular base

Second Version: Tail and rear legs
attached to an oval base

Designer: Graham Tongue
Height: 10", 25.4 cm

FIRST VERSION: *Hind legs attached to a circular base.*

Colourway	Finish	Intro.	Disc.	U.K. £	U.S. $	Can. $
White	Gloss	1974	Unknown	395.00	625.00	900.00

SECOND VERSON: *Tail and rear legs attached to an oval base.*

Colourway	Finish	Intro.	Disc.	U.K. £	U.S. $	Can. $
White	Gloss	Unknown	1981	350.00	575.00	800.00

Model No. 2505

STEEPLECHASER

Designer: Graham Tongue
Height: 8 3/4", 22.2 cm

Colourway	Finish	Intro.	Disc.	U.K. £	U.S. $	Can. $
Dark brown	Gloss	1975	1981	325.00	550.00	725.00

Model No. 2510   *RED RUM*

SERIES: *Connoisseur Horses*

Designer: Graham Tongue
Height: 12", 30.5 cm

Colourway	Finish	DA #	Intro.	Disc.	U.K. £	U.S. $	Can. $
Bay	Matt	18	1975	1989	175.00	325.00	450.00

Model No. 2511

RED RUM
BRIAN FLETCHER UP

SERIES: *Connoisseur Horses*

Designer: Graham Tongue
Height: 12 1/4", 31.1 cm

Colourway	Finish	Intro.	Disc.	U.K. £	U.S. $	Can. $
Bay	Matt	1975	1982	325.00	550.00	700.00

Model No. 2535

PSALM
ANN MOORE UP

SERIES: *Connoisseur Horses*

Designer: Graham Tongue
Height: 12 3/4", 32.4 cm

Colourway	Finish	Intro.	Disc.	U.K. £	U.S. $	Can. $
Brown	Matt	1975	1982	300.00	475.00	675.00

Model No. 2536   *"BLACK BEAUTY" FOAL*

Designer: Graham Tongue
Height: 3 1/2", 8.9 cm

Colourway	Finish	DA #	Intro.	Disc.	U.K. £	U.S. $	Can. $
Black	Matt	66	1976	1989	35.00	65.00	95.00
Brown	Matt	—	1984	Unknown	55.00	95.00	125.00
Chocolate brown	Matt	—	1984	Unknown	55.00	95.00	125.00
Palomino	Matt	—	1984	Unknown	65.00	100.00	150.00

Model No. 2540

PSALM

SERIES: Connoisseur Horses

Designer: Graham Tongue
Height: 11 1/2", 29.2 cm

Colourway	Finish	Intro.	Disc.	U.K. £	U.S. $	Can. $
Brown	Matt	1975	1982	195.00	350.00	450.00

Model No. 2541A

WELSH MOUNTAIN STALLION
"GREDINGTON SIMWNT"

This model of "Gredington Simwnt" was greatly adapted to produce "The Spirit of Whitfield".

SERIES: *Connoisseur Horses*

Designer: Graham Tongue
Height: 9", 22.9 cm

Colourway	Finish	Intro.	Disc.	U.K. £	U.S. $	Can. $
Light grey	Matt	1976	1989	180.00	350.00	475.00

Model No. 2558   *GRUNDY*

SERIES: *Connoisseur Horses*

Designer: Graham Tongue
Height: 11 1/4", 28.5 cm

Colourway	Finish	DA #	Intro.	Disc.	U.K. £	U.S. $	Can. $
Chestnut	Matt	20	1977	1989	175.00	325.00	425.00

Model No. 2562

LIFEGUARD

STYLE TWO: **With sword**

SERIES: **Connoisseur Horses**

Designer: Graham Tongue
Height: 14 1/2", 36.8 cm

Colourway	Finish	DA #	Intro.	Disc.	U.K. £	U.S. $	Can. $
Black	Gloss	22	1977	1989	350.00	550.00	750.00

Model No. 2578

SHIRE HORSE
(Large action shire)

Designer: Alan Maslankowski
Height: 8 1/4", 21.0 cm

Colourway	Finish	DA #	Intro.	Disc.	U.K. £	U.S. $	Can. $
Brown	Gloss	—	1980	1982	175.00	300.00	450.00
Brown	Matt	62	1978	1989	125.00	200.00	300.00
Grey	Gloss	—	1975	1982	125.00	200.00	300.00
Grey	Matt	—	1980	1983	165.00	250.00	400.00

SERIES: Harnessed Horses

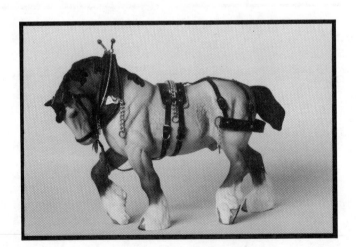

Colourway	Finish	Intro.	Disc.	U.K. £	U.S. $	Can. $
Brown	Matt	1978	1982	175.00	300.00	450.00
Grey	Matt	1978	1982	175.00	300.00	450.00

Model No. 2582

BLUES AND ROYALS

SERIES: *Connoisseur Horses*

Designer: Graham Tongue
Height: 14 1/2", 36.8 cm

Colourway	Finish	DA #	Intro.	Disc.	U.K. £	U.S. $	Can. $
Black	Matt	25	1987	1989	375.00	600.00	850.00

Model No. 2605

MORGAN STALLION
"TARRYALL MAESTRO"

SERIES: Connoisseur Horses

Designer: Graham Tongue
Height: 11 1/2", 29.2 cm

Colourway	Finish	DA #	Intro.	Disc.	U.K. £	U.S. $	Can. $
Black	Matt	28	1979	1989	150.00	275.00	375.00

Model No. 2608

THE MINSTREL

SERIES: *Connoisseur Horses*

Designer: Graham Tongue
Height: 13 1/4", 33.6 cm

Colourway	Finish	DA #	Intro.	Disc.	U.K. £	U.S. $	Can. $
Chestnut	Matt	31	1980	1989	175.00	300.00	400.00

Model No. 2671

MOONLIGHT

SERIES: *Connoisseur Horses*

Designer: Graham Tongue
Height: 11 1/4", 28.5 cm

COLOURWAY No. 1:   *"Moonlight" - Grey*

Colourway	Finish	DA #	Intro.	Disc.	U.K. £	U.S. $	Can. $
"Moonlight" - Grey	Matt	35	1986	1989	145.00	250.00	375.00

COLOURWAY No. 2:   *"Sunburst" - Palomino*

Colourway	Finish	DA #	Intro.	Disc.	U.K. £	U.S. $	Can. $
"Sunburst" - Palomino	Mat	36	1986	1989	145.00	250.00	375.00

COLOURWAY No. 3:   *"Nightshade" - Black*

Colourway	Finish	Intro.	Disc.	U.K. £	U.S. $	Can. $
"Nightshade" - Black	Matt	1986	1989	145.00	250.00	375.00

Model No. 2674   *TROY*

SERIES: *Connoisseur Horses*

Designer: Graham Tongue
Height: 11 3/4", 29.8 cm

Colourway	Finish	DA #	Intro.	Disc.	U.K. £	U.S. $	Can. $
Bay	Matt	37	1981	1989	175.00	300.00	400.00

Model No. 2688   *SPIRIT OF THE WIND*

Designer: Graham Tongue
Height: 8", 20.3 cm

Colourway	Finish	DA #	Intro.	Disc.	U.K. £	U.S. $	Can. $
Brown	Gloss	57	1982	1989	65.00	125.00	175.00
Brown	Matt	57	1982	1989	65.00	125.00	175.00
Grey	Gloss	—	1982	1989	85.00	175.00	225.00
Grey	Matt	—	1982	1989	75.00	150.00	200.00
Palomino	Gloss	—	1982	1989	65.00	125.00	175.00
Palomino	Matt	—	1982	1989	75.00	150.00	200.00

SERIES: *On Wooden Plinth*

Colourway	Finish	DA #	Intro.	Disc.	U.K. £	U.S. $	Can. $
Black	Matt	57	1986	1989	75.00	150.00	200.00
Brown	Matt	57	1986	1989	85.00	175.00	225.00
White	Matt	57	1982	1989	75.00	150.00	200.00

SERIES: *On Ceramic Plinth*

Colourway	Finish	Intro.	Disc.	U.K. £	U.S. $	Can. $
Brown	Gloss	c.1987	c.1987	85.00	175.00	225.00

SERIES: *Britannia Collection*

Colourway	Finish	Intro.	Disc.	U.K. £	U.S. $	Can. $
Brown	Gloss	1989	1993	75.00	150.00	200.00

Model No. 2689   *SPIRIT OF FREEDOM*

Model number 2689 was used together with model number 2353 to become the Spirit of Affection.

Designer: Graham Tongue
Height: 7", 17.8 cm

Colourway	Finish	DA #	Intro.	Disc.	U.K. £	U.S. $	Can. $
Brown	Gloss	58	1982	1989	65.00	125.00	175.00
Brown	Matt	58	1982	1989	65.00	125.00	175.00
Grey	Gloss	—	1982	1989	85.00	175.00	225.00
Grey	Matt	—	1982	1989	75.00	150.00	200.00
Palomino	Gloss	—	1982	1989	65.00	125.00	175.00
Palomino	Matt	—	1982	1989	75.00	150.00	200.00

SERIES: On Wooden Plinth

The black and brown versions were mounted on brown wooden plinths and the white version was issued on a black wooden plinth.

Colourway	Finish	DA #	Intro.	Disc.	U.K. £	U.S. $	Can. $
Black	Matt	58	1987	1989	75.00	150.00	200.00
Brown	Matt	58	1986	1989	85.00	175.00	225.00
White	Matt	58	1982	1989	75.00	150.00	200.00

SERIES: On Ceramic Plinth

Colourway	Finish	Intro.	Disc.	U.K. £	U.S. $	Can. $
Brown	Gloss	c.1987	c.1987	85.00	175.00	225.00

Model No. 2689/2353

SPIRIT OF AFFECTION

The Spirit of Affection is the Spirit of Freedom with the Black Beauty Foal. In all versions but one, the mare and the foal are the same colour. The brown, grey and palomino versions were mounted on a brown wooden plinth and the white version was mounted on a black wooden plinth.

SERIES: *On Wooden Plinth*

Designer: Graham Tongue
Height: 8", 20.3 cm

Colourway	Finish	DA #	Intro.	Disc.	U.K. £	U.S. $	Can. $
Brown	Matt	64	1984	1989	95.00	150.00	225.00
Grey mare, chocolate brown foal	Matt	—	1984	1989	110.00	175.00	250.00
Palomino	Matt	—	1984	1989	110.00	175.00	250.00
White	Matt	64	1984	1989	85.00	135.00	200.00

Model No. 2703   *SPIRIT OF YOUTH*

The Spirit of Youth is the same model as 2466 "Black Beauty".

Designer: Graham Tongue
Height: 7", 17.8 cm

Colourway	Finish	DA #	Intro.	Disc.	U.K. £	U.S. $	Can. $
Brown	Gloss	59	1982	1989	65.00	125.00	175.00
Brown	Matt	59	1982	1989	65.00	125.00	175.00
Grey	Gloss	—	1982	1989	85.00	175.00	225.00
Grey	Matt	—	1982	1989	75.00	150.00	200.00
Palomino	Gloss	—	1092	1989	65.00	125.00	175.00
Palomino	Matt	—	1982	1989	75.00	150.00	200.00

SERIES: *On Wooden Plinth.*

The black and brown models were issued on a wooden plinth and the white model was issued o a black wooden plinth.

Colourway	Finish	DA #	Intro.	Disc.	U.K. £	U.S. $	Can. $
Black	Matt	59	1987	1989	75.00	150.00	200.00
Brown	Matt	59	1986	1989	85.00	175.00	225.00
White	Matt	59	1982	1989	75.00	150.00	200.00

SERIES: *On Ceramic Plinth*

Colourway	Finish	Intro.	Disc.	U.K. £	U.S. $	Can. $
Brown	Gloss	c.1987	c.1987	85.00	175.00	225.00

Model No. 2829   *SPIRIT OF FIRE*

Designer: Graham Tongue
Height: 8", 20.3 cm

Colourway	Finish	DA #	Intro.	Disc.	U.K. £	U.S. $	Can. $
Brown	Gloss	60	1984	1989	65.00	125.00	175.00
Brown	Matt	60	1984	1989	65.00	125.00	175.00
Grey	Gloss	—	1984	1989	85.00	175.00	225.00
Grey	Matt	—	1984	1989	75.00	150.00	200.00
Palomino	Gloss	—	1984	1989	65.00	125.00	175.00
Palomino	Matt	—	1984	1989	75.00	150.00	200.00

SERIES: *On Wooden Plinths*

The black and brown versions were issued on a brown wooden plinth and the white version was issued on a black wooden plinth.

Colourway	Finish	DA #	Intro.	Disc.	U.K. £	U.S. $	Can. $
Black	Matt	60	1986	1989	75.00	150.00	200.00
Brown	Matt	60	1986	1989	85.00	175.00	225.00
White	Matt	60	1984	1989	75.00	150.00	200.00

SERIES: *On Ceramic Plinth*

Colourway	Finish	Intro.	Disc.	U.K. £	U.S. $	Can. $
Brown	Gloss	c.1987	c.1987	85.00	175.00	225.00

Model No. 2837   *SPRINGTIME*

SERIES: *Spirited Foals*

Designer: Graham Tongue
Height: 4 1/2"

VARIATION No. 1:   *Free standing*

Colourway	Finish	DA #	Intro.	Disc.	U.K. £	U.S. $	Can. $
Brown	Gloss	69	1984	1989	25.00	40.00	60.00

VARIATION No. 2:   *On wooden plinth*

Colourway	Finish	DA #	Intro.	Disc.	U.K. £	U.S. $	Can. $
Black (wooden plinth)	Matt	—	1987	1989	35.00	55.00	75.00
Brown (wooden plinth	Matt	69	1986	1989	25.00	40.00	60.00
White (black plinth)	Matt	69	1984	1989	25.00	40.00	60.00

Model No. 2839

YOUNG SPIRIT

"Young Spirit" was originally illustrated in a catalogue with his ears sticking out slightly. The model was changed to have the ears flat against the foals head, probably due to the potential problem of breakage in shipping. No date has been established for the mould change but it is probably either in the early stages of production i.e. proto-type or shortly after issue.

SERIES: *Spirited Foals*

Designer: Graham Tongue
Height: 4 1/2", 11.9 cm

VARIATION No. 1: *Free standing*

Colourway	Finish	DA #	Intro.	Disc.	U.K. £	U.S. $	Can. $
Brown	Gloss	70	1984	1989	30.00	45.00	65.00

VARIATION No. 2: *On wooden plinth*

Colourway	Finish	DA #	Intro.	Disc.	U.K. £	U.S. $	Can. $
Black (wooden plinth)	Matt	70	1987	1989	25.00	40.00	55.00
Brown (wooden plinth)	Matt	70	1986	1989	25.00	40.00	55.00
White (black plinth)	Matt	70	1984	1989	25.00	40.00	55.00

Model No. 2875

SUNLIGHT

SERIES: *Spirited Foals*

Designer: Graham Tongue
Height: 4 1/2", 11.9 cm

VARIATION No. 1: *Free standing*

Colourway	Finish	DA #	Intro.	Disc.	U.K. £	U.S. $	Can. $
Brown	Gloss	71	1987	1989	20.00	35.00	45.00

VARIATION No. 2 *On wooden plinth*

Colourway	Finish	DA #	Intro.	Disc.	U.K. £	U.S. $	Can. $
Black (wooden plinth)	Matt	71	1987	1989	25.00	40.00	55.00
Brown (woooden plinth)	Matt	71	1987	1989	25.00	40.00	55.00
White (black plinth)	Matt	71	1985	1989	25.00	40.00	55.00

Model No. 2876

ADVENTURE

SERIES: **Spirited Foals**

Designer: Graham Tongue
Height: 4 1/2", 11.9 cm

VARIATION No. 1:   *Free standing*

Colourway	Finish	DA #	Intro.	Disc.	U.K. £	U.S. $	Can. $
Brown	Gloss	72	1987	1989	20.00	35.00	45.00

VARIATION No. 2:   *On wooden plinths.*

Colourway	Finish	DA #	Intro.	Disc.	U.K. £	U.S. $	Can. $
Black	Matt	—	1987	1989	25.00	40.00	55.00
Brown	Matt	72	1987	1989	25.00	40.00	55.00
White	Matt	72	1985	1989	25.00	40.00	55.00

Model No. 2914   *SPIRIT OF EARTH*

Designer: Graham Tongue
Height: 7 1/2", 19.1 cm

Colourway	Finish	DA #	Intro.	Disc.	U.K. £	U.S. $	Can. $
Brown	Gloss	61	1987	1989	45.00	75.00	100.00
Brown	Matt	61	1987	1989	55.00	85.00	125.00
Grey	Gloss	—	1987	1989	75.00	125.00	175.00
Grey	Matt	—	1987	1989	65.00	100.00	150.00

SERIES: On Wooden Plinths

The black and brown versions were issued on a brown wooden plinth and the white version was issued on a black wooden plinth.

Colourway	Finish	Intro.	Disc.	U.K. £	U.S. $	Can. $
Black	Matt	1987	1989	60.00	95.00	125.00
Brown	Matt	1987	1989	60.00	95.00	125.00
White	Matt	1986	1989	60.00	95.00	125.00

SERIES: On Ceramic Plinth

Colourway	Finish	Intro.	Disc.	U.K. £	U.S. $	Can. $
Brown	Gloss	c.1987	c.1987	60.00	95.00	125.00

SERIES: Britannia Collection

Colourway	Finish	Intro.	Disc.	U.K. £	U.S. $	Can. $
Brown	Gloss	1989	1993	55.00	85.00	125.00

Model No. 2916   *SPIRIT OF PEACE*

Designer: Graham Tongue
Height: 4 3/4", 12.1 cm

Colourway	Finish	DA #	Intro.	Disc.	U.K. £	U.S. $	Can. $
Brown	Gloss	—	1987	1989	45.00	75.00	100.00
Brown	Matt	63	1987	1989	45.00	75.00	100.00
Grey	Gloss	—	1987	1989	55.00	85.00	125.00
Grey	Matt	—	1987	1989	55.00	85.00	125.00
Palomino	Gloss	—	1987	1989	50.00	85.00	125.00
Palomino	Matt	—	1987	1989	50.00	85.00	125.00

SERIES: *On Wooden Plinths*

The black and brown versions were issued on a brown wooden plinth and the white version was issued on a black wooden plinth.

Colourway	Finish	DA #	Intro.	Disc.	U.K. £	U.S. $	Can. $
Black	Matt	—	1987	1989	55.00	85.00	125.00
Brown	Matt	63	1987	1989	50.00	80.00	115.00
White	Matt	63	1986	1989	45.00	75.00	100.00

SERIES: *On Ceramic Plinth*

Colourway	Finish	Intro.	Disc.	U.K. £	U.S. $	Can. $
Brown	Gloss	c.1987	c.1987	60.00	95.00	125.00

Model No. 2935   *SPIRIT OF NATURE*

Designer: Graham Tongue
Height: 5 1/2", 14.0 cm

Colourway	Finish	Intro.	Disc.	U.K. £	U.S. $	Can. $
Brown	Gloss	1987	1989	50.00	80.00	115.00
Brown	Matt	1987	1989	50.00	80.00	115.00
Grey	Gloss	1987	1989	60.00	95.00	135.00
Grey	Matt	1987	1989	60.00	95.00	135.00
Palomino	Gloss	1987	1989	55.00	85.00	125.00
Palomino	Matt	1987	1989	55.00	85.00	125.00

SERIES: On Wooden Plinth

The black and brown versions were mounted on brown wooden plinths and the white version was mounted on a black wooden plinth.

Colourway	Finish	DA #	Intro.	Disc.	U.K. £	U.S. $	Can. $
Black	Matt	—	1987	1989	60.00	95.00	125.00
Brown	Matt	73	1987	1989	60.00	95.00	125.00
White	Matt	—	1987	1989	50.00	80.00	115.00

SERIES: On Ceramic Plinth

Colourway	Finish	Intro.	Disc.	U.K. £	U.S. $	Can. $
Brown	Gloss	c.1987	c.1987	60.00	95.00	125.00

Model No. 3426

CANCARA

Modelled from "Downland Cancara" graded Trakehner stallion famous for advertising Lloyds Bank. Backstamp - "1994 Special Beswick Centenary".

> *SERIES:* ***On wooden plinth***

Designer: Graham Tongue
Height: 16 1/2", 41.9 cm

Colourway	Finish	DA #	Intro.	Disc.	U.K. £	U.S. $	Can. $
Black	Matt	234	1994	1994	300.00	475.00	675.00

Model No. 3464   *TALLY HO*

Made exclusively for the mail order catalogue company Grattans. The horse and rider, from the model 868 "Rearing Huntsman", with three hounds are on a natural effect base (all gloss). This model stands on a wooden plinth which is topped with green baise and has a brass plaque on the front. Backstamp - "Beswick Ware Made in England Tally Ho! Beswick Centenary 1894-1994 © 1994 Royal Doulton."

Designer: Unknown
Height: 11" x 14", 27.9 x 35.5 cm

Colourway	Finish	Intro.	Disc.	U.K. £	U.S. $	Can. $
Brown	Gloss	1994	1994	200.00	350.00	475.00

HOLLYDELL DIXIE
(Shetland Pony)

This model is a Beswick Collectors Circle special to be issued in August 1995. This model will be especially decorated to represent Shetland Mare Supreme Champion "Hollydell Dixie".

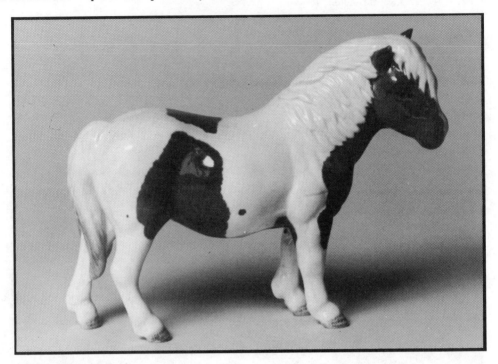

Designer: Amanda Hughes-Lubeck
Height: 5 1/4", 13.3 cm

Colourway	Finish	DA #	Intro.	Disc.	U.K. £	U.S. $	Can. $
Skewbald	Gloss	185	1995	1995	32.00	N/A	N/A

"SPIRIT OF WHITFIELD"

Commissioned for the Chatterley Whitfield Minig Museum.

Designer: Graham Tongue
Height: 9", 22.9 cm

Colourway	Finish	Intro.	Disc.	U.K. £	U.S. $	Can. $
Brown	Matt	1987	1987		Only four exist	

WALL ORNAMENTS
- HORSES

INDEX BY MODEL NUMBER

Photograph not
available at press time

Photograph not
available at press time

Model No. 686
HORSE'S HEAD LOOKING LEFT THROUGH A
HORSESHOE
First Version - Flat back

Designer:	Mr. Owen
Height:	7 1/4" x 6", 18.4 x 15.0 cm
Colour:	1: Brown - gloss
	2: Dark chestnut - gloss
Issued:	1938-1939
Varieties:	807

Description:	U.K. £	U.S. $	Can. $
1: Brown			
2: Dark chestnut		Extremely Rare	

Model No. 687
HORSE'S HEAD LOOKING RIGHT THROUGH A
HORSESHOE
First Version - Flat back

Designer:	Mr. Owen
Height:	7 1/4" x 6", 18.4 x 15.0 cm
Colour:	1: Brown - gloss
	2: Dark chestnut - gloss
Issued:	1939 - 1939
Varieties:	806

Description:	U.K. £	U.S. $	Can. $
1: Brown			
2: Dark chestnut		Extremely Rare	

Model No. 806
HORSE'S HEAD LOOKING RIGHT THROUGH A
HORSESHOE
Second Version - Raised back

Designer:	Mr. Owen
Height:	7 1/4" x 6", 18.4 x 15.0 cm
Colour:	Brown - gloss
Issued:	1939 - 1968
Varieties:	687

Description:	U.K. £	U.S. $	Can. $
Gloss	100.00	175.00	275.00

Model No. 807
HORSE'S HEAD LOOKING LEFT THROUGH A
HORSESHOE
Second Version - Raised back

Designer:	Mr. Owen
Height:	7 1/4" x 6", 18.4 x 15.0 cm
Colour:	Brown - gloss
Issued:	1938-1968
Varieties:	686

Description:	U.K. £	U.S. $	Can. $
Gloss	100.00	175.00	275.00

Model No. 1382
HUNTER HEAD

Designer: Arthur Gredington
Height: 4" x 4", 10.1 x 10.1 cm
Colour: Brown - gloss
Issued: 1955-1969

Description:	*U.K. £*	*U.S. $*	*Can. $*
Gloss	95.00	150.00	200.00

Model No. 1384
PALOMINO HEAD

Designer: Arthur Gredington
Height: 4" x 4", 10.1 x 10.1 cm
Colour: Palomino - gloss
Issued: 1955-1969

Description:	*U.K. £*	*U.S. $*	*Can. $*
Gloss	95.00	150.00	200.00

Model No. 1385
ARAB HEAD

Designer:	Arthur Gredington
Height:	4" x 4", 10.1 x 10.1 cm
Colour:	Dark Brown - gloss
Issued:	1955-1969

Description:	U.K. £	U.S. $	Can. $
Gloss	95.00	150.00	200.00

Model No. 1505
HUNTSMAN

Designer:	Mr. Hayward and Albert Hallam
Height:	8 1/2", 21.6 cm
Colour:	1: Brown - gloss
	2: Copper lustre
Issued:	1958-1962

Description:	U.K. £	U.S. $	Can. $
1: Brown	175.00	300.00	400.00
2: Copper lustre	150.00	250.00	350.00

Model No. 1513
"TAKING OFF"
Designer: Colin Melbourne
Height: 9", 22.9 cm
Colour: 1: Brown - gloss
                   2: Copper lustre
Issued: 1958-1962

Description:	U.K. £	U.S. $	Can. $
1: Brown	175.00	300.00	400.00
2: Copper lustre	150.00	250.00	350.00

Model No. 1514
"LANDING"
Designer: Colin Melbourne
Height: 7 3/4, 19.7 cm
Colour: 1: Brown - gloss
                    2: Copper lustre
Issued: 1958-1962

Description:	U.K. £	U.S. $	Can. $
1: Brown	175.00	300.00	400.00
2: Copper lustre	150.00	250.00	350.00

Model No. 1515
"GOING OVER"
Designer: Colin Melbourne
Height: 7 1/2", 19.1 cm
Colour: 1: Brown - gloss
                    2: Copper lustre
Issued: 1958-1962

Description:	U.K. £	U.S. $	Can. $
1: Brown	175.00	300.00	400.00
2: Copper lustre	150.00	250.00	350.00

Model No. 2699
TROY

Designer: Unknown
Height: 6", 15.0 cm
Colour: Brown - matt
Issued: 1984-1989
Series: "Champions All"

Description:	U.K. £	U.S. $	Can. $
Matt	50.00	75.00	100.00

Model No. 2700
ARKLE

Designer: Unknown
Height: 6", 15.0 cm
Colour: Bay - matt
Issued: 1984-1989
Series: "Champions All"

Description:	U.K. £	U.S. $	Can. $
Matt	50.00	75.00	100.00

Model No. 2701
THE MINSTREL

Designer:	Unknown
Height:	6", 15.0 cm
Colour:	Chestnut - matt
Issued:	1984-1989
Series:	"Champions All"

Description:	U.K. £	U.S. $	Can. $
Matt	50.00	75.00	100.00

Model No. 2702
RED RUM

Designer:	Unknown
Height:	6", 15.0 cm
Colour:	Bay - matt
Issued:	1984-1989
Series:	"Champions All"

Description:	U.K. £	U.S. $	Can. $
Matt	50.00	75.00	100.00

MISCELLANEOUS

INDEX BY MODEL NUMBER

Model No. 2093
OLD STAFFORDSHIRE LION

Designer: Graham Tongue
Height: 5 3/4", 14.6 cm
Colour: Grey, cream, green - gloss
Issued: 1967-1971

Description:	U.K. £	U.S. $	Can. $
Gloss		Extremely Rare	

Model No. 2094
OLD STAFFORDSHIRE UNICORN

Designer: Graham Tongue
Height: 6", 15.0 cm
Colour: Grey, cream, green - gloss
Issued: 1967-1971

Description:	U.K. £	U.S. $	Can. $
Gloss		Extremely Rare	

Photograph not
available at press time

Model No. 2137
T'ANG HORSE - Small

Designer: Graham Tongue
Height: 8", 20.3 cm
Colourway Green/bronze - gloss
Issued: 1967-1972

Description:	U.K. £	U.S. $	Can. $
Gloss	200.00	350.00	450.00

Model No. 2182
HERALDIC UNICORN ON BASE

Designer: Graham Tongue
Height: 8 1/2", 21.6 cm
Colour.   Unknown
Issued: Unknown

Description:	U.K. £	U.S. $	Can. $
		Extremely Rare	

Model No. 2205
T'ANG HORSE- Large

Designer:	Graham Tongue
Height:	13", 33.0 cm
Colour:	Green/bronze - gloss
Issued:	1968-1972

Description:	U.K. £	U.S. $	Can. $
Gloss	300.00	500.00	675.00

Photograph not
available at press time

Model No. 2223
UNICORN

Designer:	Mrs. Elliott
Height:	4", 10.1 cm
Colour.	Cream - matt
Issued:	1968-Unknown

Description:	U.K. £	U.S. $	Can. $
Matt		Extremely Rare	

Model No. 2514
WHITE HORSE WHISKY

Designer:	Alan Maslankowski
Height:	6 3/4", 17.2 cm
Colour:	White - gloss
Issued:	1974
Series:	Advertising

Description:	U.K. £	U.S. $	Can. $
Gloss	400.00	600.00	900.00

Model No. 3021
UNICORN

Designer:	Graham Tongue
Height:	9", 2.9 cm
Colour:	1: Cream - matt
	2: Dark bronze - gloss
Issued:	1989-Unknown
Series:	Britannia Collection

Description:	U.K. £	U.S. $	Can. $
1: Cream	150.00	275.00	375.00
2: Dark Bronze	80.00	125.00	175.00

Chapter Eight

WILD ANIMALS

The wild animals in this group have been produced by John Beswick for more than fifty years. Many are authentic and true to life in shape and colour, others are comical.

Beswick wild animals are very popular with collectors. They are less of a minefield for the inexperienced than some of the other series, as the animals are familiar and can be easily identified, since most carry the Beswick backstamp.

As you can see, Beswick produced these animals in a random order. It was not until the late 1930s that realism was created by the use of natural colours, instead of the very popular blue gloss used in earlier days. Around this time, the models were also refined to represent real animals.

The variety of animals is enormous and most animals are represented, ranging from the smallest mouse to the very large African elephant. The powerful bison, the gentle springbok and the elegant giraffe are just some of these superb pieces.

At the time of the introduction of the *Connoisseur Series* in 1967, most of the items were horses, and it was not until 1973 that three wild animals were absorbed into the series. These were the already existing versions of two elephants, numbers 998 and 1770, both free standing, and a puma on a rock, number 1702. As the name suggests, the *Connoisseur Series* comprises prestige models, and consequently were and are more expensive than the rest of the animals.

It is interesting to note that Mr. Gredington was the modeller responsible for the majority of the wild animals. Some collectors collect models from one particular designer or modeller, and these would make an excellent choice.

Many of the wild animals are avidly sought after. The search is a challenge, but well worth the effort if you can find your treasured piece.

INDEX BY MODEL NUMBER

Model No. 315
SQUIRREL - On pottery base

Designer:	Miss Greaves
Height:	8 3/4", 22.2 cm
Colour:	1: Cream - satin matt
	2: Blue - gloss
Issued:	1935-By 1954

Description:	U.K. £	U.S. $	Can. $
1: Cream	100.00	160.00	225.00
2: Blue	125.00	200.00	300.00

Note: Possibly other colourways exist.

Model No. 368
FROG - On pottery base

Designer:	Miss Greaves
Height:	6 3/4", 16.5 cm
Colour:	Brown, cream or green - satin matt
	Blue - gloss
Issued:	1936-By 1954

Description:	U.K. £	U.S. $	Can. $
1: Brown	110.00	175.00	250.00
2: Cream	110.00	175.00	250.00
3: Green	110.00	175.00	250.00
3: Blue	110.00	175.00	250.00

Note: Possibly other colourways exist.

Model No. 316
RABBIT - On pottery base

Designer:	Miss Greaves
Height:	6 3/4", 17.2 cm
Colour:	1: Cream - satin matt
	2: Blue - gloss
Issued:	1935-By 1954

Description:	U.K. £	U.S. $	Can. $
1: Cream	125.00	200.00	300.00
2: Blue	140.00	225.00	350.00

Note: Possibly other colourways exist.

Model No. 383
SEAL - On pottery base

Designer:	Mr. Owen
Height:	10", 25.4 cm
Colour:	1: Cream - satin matt
	2: Blue - gloss
Issued:	1936-By 1954

Description:	U.K. £	U.S. $	Can. $
1: Cream	110.00	175.00	250.00
2: Blue	110.00	175.00	250.00

Note: Possibly other colourways exist.

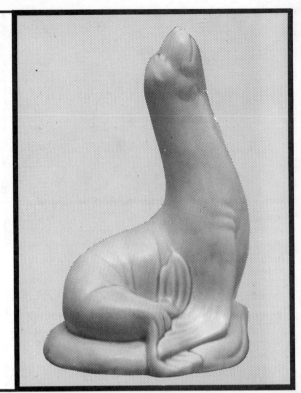

Model No. 397
MONKEY - On pottery base

Designer:	Mr. Owen
Height:	7", 17.8 cm
Colour:	1: Cream - satin matt
	2: Blue - gloss
Issued:	1936-By 1954

Description:	U.K. £	U.S. $	Can. $
1: Cream	110.00	175.00	250.00
2: Blue	120.00	200.00	300.00

Note: Possibly other colourways exist.

Model No. 417
POLAR BEAR - On pottery base

Designer:	Mr. Owen		
Height:	7", 17.8 cm		
Colour:	1: White - satin matt		
	2: Blue - gloss		
Issued:	1936-By 1954		

Description:	*U.K. £*	*U.S. $*	*Can. $*
1: White	125.00	200.00	300.00
2: Blue	120.00	200.00	300.00

Photograph not
available at press time

Model No. 568
CHARACTER ELEPHANT - Large

Designer:	Mr. Owen
Height:	9", 22.9 cm
Colour:	Blue - gloss
Issued:	1938-By 1954
Set:	569

Description:	*U.K. £*	*U.S. $*	*Can. $*
Gloss	175.00	275.00	400.00

Model No. 569
CHARACTER ELEPHANT - Small

Designer:	Mr. Owen
Height:	4 3/4", 12.1 cm
Colour:	Blue - gloss
Issued:	1938-By 1954
Set:	568

Description:	*U.K. £*	*U.S. $*	*Can. $*
Gloss	110.00	175.00	250.00

Model No. 692
ELEPHANT WITH HOWDAH

Designer:	Unkown
Height:	4 1/4", 10.8 cm
Colour:	Blue - gloss
Issued:	1939-By 1954

Description:	*U.K. £*	*U.S. $*	*Can. $*
Gloss		Extremely Rare	

Model No. 696
DEER ON ROCK

Designer:	Arthur Gredington		
Height:	8", 20.3 cm		
Colour:	See below		
Issued:	1939-1954		
Set:	Companion piece to 721		

Description:	U.K. £	U.S. $	Can. $
1: Brown- gloss	110.00	175.00	225.00
2: Blue - gloss	110.00	225.00	325.00
3: Flambé - gloss	160.00	250.00	350.00
4: White - gloss	110.00	175.00	225.00

Model No. 697
HIPPOPOTAMUS

Designer:	Mr. Watkin
Height:	2 1/4"", 5.7 cm
Colour:	Blue - gloss
Issued:	1939-By 1954
Series:	Fun Models

Description:	U.K. £	U.S. $	Can. $
Gloss	120.00	200.00	275.00

Photograph not
available at press time

Model No. 698
GIRAFFE

Designer:	Mr. Watkin
Height:	4", 10.1 cm
Colour:	Blue - gloss
Issued:	1939-By 1954
Series:	Fun Models

Description:	U.K. £	U.S. $	Can. $
Gloss	75.00	125.00	225.00

Model No. 709
BEAVER

Designer:	Mr. Watkin
Height:	Unknown
Colour:	Unknown
Issued:	1939-Unknown

Description:	U.K. £	U.S. $	Can. $
	Extremely Rare		

Note: Possibly not put into production.

Model No. 711
PANDA

Designer:	Mr.Watkin
Height:	4 1/2", 11.9 cm
Colour:	Black and white - gloss
Issued:	1939-By 1954

Description:	U.K. £	U.S. $	Can. $
Gloss	95.00	150.00	200.00

Model No. 720
PANDA CUB

Designer:	Mr.Haywood
Height:	3 3/4", 9.5 cm
Colour:	Black and white - gloss
	Cream - Satin matt
Issued:	1939-By 1954

Description:	U.K. £	U.S. $	Can. $
1: Gloss	95.00	150.00	200.00
2: Satin matt	75.00	125.00	175.00

Model No. 721
DEER ON BASE

Designer:	Arthur Gredington
Height:	4 1/2", 11.9 cm
Colour:	1: Brown - gloss
	2: Blue - gloss
	3: White - matt
Issued:	1939-By 1954
Set:	Companion piece with 696

Description:	U.K. £	U.S. $	Can. $
1: Brown	100.00	160.00	225.00
2: Blue	110.00	175.00	275.00
3: White	100.00	160.00	225.00

Model No. 738
PANDA

Designer:	Mr. Watkin
Height:	4 1/2", 11.9 cm
Colour:	1: Black and white - gloss
	2: Cream - gloss
	3: Blue - gloss
Issued:	1939-By 1954

Description:	U.K. £	U.S. $	Can. $
1: Black/white	95.00	150.00	200.00
2: Cream	75.00	125.00	175.00
3: Blue	95.00	150.00	200.00

Model No. 823
RABBIT - On haunches

Designer:	Arthur Gredington
Height:	3", 7.6 cm
Colour:	1: Brown - gloss
	2: Blue - gloss
Issued:	1940-1971
Set:	824, 825, 826

Description:	U.K. £	U.S. $	Can. $
1: Brown	30.00	50.00	70.00
2: Blue	35.00	55.00	90.00

Model No. 824
RABBIT - Scratching ear

Designer:	Arthur Gredington
Height:	2 1/4", 5.7 cm
Colour:	1: Brown - gloss
	2: Blue - gloss
Issued:	1940-1971
Set:	823, 825, 826

Description:	U.K. £	U.S. $	Can. $
1: Brown	35.00	55.00	75.00
2: Blue	30.00	50.00	75.00

Model No. 825
RABBIT - Crouching

Designer:	Arthur Gredington
Height:	1 1/2", 3.8 cm
Colour:	1: Brown - gloss
	2: Blue - gloss
Issued:	1940-1971
Set:	823, 824, 826

Description:	U.K. £	U.S. $	Can. $
1: Brown	35.00	55.00	75.00
2: Blue	30.00	50.00	75.00

Model No. 826
RABBIT - Seated

Designer:	Arthur Gredington
Height:	2", 5.0 cm
Colour:	1: Brown - gloss
	2: Blue - gloss
Issued:	1940-1971
Set:	823, 824, 825

Description:	U.K. £	U.S. $	Can. $
1: Brown	35.00	55.00	75.00
2: Blue	30.00	50.00	75.00

Model No. 828

ELEPHANT

Designer:	Mr. Owen
Height:	See below
Colour:	Pale grey - gloss
Issued:	1940-By 1954
Set:	568

			Price	
Description	*Height*	*U.K. £*	*U.S. $*	*Can. $*
1: Large	6", 15.0 cm	95.00	150.00	250.00
2: Medium	4 1/2", 11.9 m	75.00	125.00	175.00
3: Small	3", 7.6 cm	65.00	110.00	175.00

Model No. 830
LIZARD

Designer:	Miss Joachim
Height:	Unknown
Colour:	Unknown
Issued:	1940-Unknown

Description:	*U.K. £*	*U.S. $*	*Can. $*
		Extremely Rare	

Model No. 841
LEOPARD - Seated

Designer:	Arthur Gredington
Height:	6 1/4", 15.9 cm
Colour:	Tan brown, black spots - gloss
Issued:	1940-By 1954

Description:.	*U.K. £*	*U.S. $*	*Can. $*
Gloss	150.00	250.00	350.00

Model No. 845A
ZEBRA
Version One - Tan with black stripes

Designer:	Arthur Gredington
Height:	7 1/4", 18.4 cm
Colour:	Tan with black stripes - gloss
Issued:	1940-Unknown

Description	*U.K. £*	*U.S. $*	*Can. $*
Tan/black stripes	175.00	275.00	400.00

Model No. 845B
ZEBRA
Version Two - White with black stripes

Designer:	Arthur Gredington
Height:	7 1/4", 18.4 cm
Colour:	White with black stripes - gloss
Issued:	Unknown-1969

Description	*U.K. £*	*U.S. $*	*Can. $*
White/black stripes	150.00	240.00	325.00

Model No. 853
GIRAFFE - Small
Designer: Arthur Gredington
Height: 7 1/4", 18.4 cm
Colour: Light brown with dark brown
              patches - gloss
Issued: 1940-1975

Description:	U.K. £	U.S. $	Can. $
Gloss	100.00	160.00	225.00

Model No. 954
STAG - Lying
Designer: Arthur Gredington
Height: 5 1/2", 14.0 cm
Colour: Light brown - gloss
Issued: 1941-1975

Description:	U.K. £	U.S. $	Can. $
Gloss	85.00	135.00	175.00

Model No. 974
ELEPHANT - Trunk stretching - small
Designer: Arthur Gredington
Height: 4 3/4", 12.1 cm
Colour: Grey - gloss or matt
Issued: 1: Gloss - 1943 to the present
              2: Matt - 1985-1988

Description:	U.K. £	U.S. $	Can. $
1: Gloss	19.95	N/A	N/A
2: Matt	30.00	50.00	75.00

Model No. 981
STAG - Standing

Designer:	Arthur Gredington
Height:	8", 20.3 cm
Colour:	Light brown - gloss or matt
Issued:	1: Gloss - 1942 to the present
	2: Matt - 1985-1988

Description:	U.K. £	U.S. $	Can. $
1: Gloss	23.00	N/A	N/A
2: Matt	35.00	60.00	75.00

Model No. 998
ELEPHANT - Trunk stretching - large

Designer:	Arthur Gredington
Height:	10 1/4", 26.0 cm
Colour:	Natural - gloss or satin matt
Issued:	1: Gloss - 1943-1975
	2: Satin matt - 1970-1973
Series:	Model in satin matt finish was transferred to Connoisseur Series in 1973.

Description:	U.K. £	U.S. $	Can. $
1: Gloss	175.00	275.00	395.00
2: Satin matt	175.00	275.00	395.00

Model No. 999A
DOE

Designer:	Arthur Gredington
Height:	6", 15.0 cm
Colour:	1: Light brown - gloss
	2: Light and dark brown - matt
Issued:	1: Gloss - 1943 to the present
	2: Matt - 1985-1988

Description:	U.K. £	U.S. $	Can. $
1: Gloss	19.95	N/A	N/A
2: Matt	30.00	50.00	70.00

Model No. 999B
DOE AND FAWN - on wooden plinth

Designer:	Arthur Gredington
Height:	7", 17.8 cm
Colour:	Light brown - gloss
Issued:	1993 to the present

Description:	U.K. £	U.S. $	Can. $
Gloss	35.00	N/A	N/A

Note: Doe is no. 999, Fawn is no. 1000

Photograph not
available at press time

Model No. 1000A
FAWN
Version One

Designer:	Arthur Gredington
Height:	3 1/2", 8.9 cm
Colour:	Light brown - gloss
Issued:	1943-1955

Description:	U.K. £	U.S. $	Can. $
Gloss	35.00	55.00	75.00

Model No. 1000B
FAWN
Version Two

Designer:	Arthur Gredington
Re-modelled:	Mr. Orwell
Height:	3 1/2", 8.9 cm
Colour:	Light brown - gloss or matt
Issued:	1: Gloss - 1955 to the present
	2: Matt - 1985-1988

Description:	U.K. £	U.S. $	Can. $
1: Gloss	10.95	N/A	N/A
2: Matt	15.00	25.00	35.00

Model No. 1003
FAWNIE

Designer:	Arthur Gredington
Height:	5 1/4", 13.3 cm
Colour:	Grey-brown - gloss
Issued:	1944-1967
Series:	Fun Models

Description:	U.K. £	U.S. $	Can. $
Gloss	75.00	125.00	165.00

Model No. 1005
KANGARINE

Designer:	Arthur Gredington
Height:	5", 12.7 cm
Colour:	Brown - gloss
Issued:	1944-1966
Series:	Fun Models

Description:	U.K. £	U.S. $	Can. $
Gloss	75.00	125.00	165.00

Model No. 1007
SQUIRREL - Standing

Designer:	Arthur Gredington
Height:	2 1/4", 5.7 cm
Colour:	Tan - gloss
Issued:	1944-c.1963
Set:	1008, 1009
Series:	Fun Models

Description:	U.K. £	U.S. $	Can. $
Gloss	45.00	70.00	100.00

Model No. 1008
SQUIRREL - Lying

Designer:	Arthur Gredington
Height:	1 3/4", 4.5 cm
Colour:	Tan - gloss
Issued:	1944-c.1963
Set:	1007, 1009
Series:	Fun Models

Description:	U.K. £	U.S. $	Can. $
Gloss	45.00	70.00	100.00

Model No. 1009
SQUIRREL - With Nut Cracker

Designer:	Arthur Gredington
Height:	4 1/2", 11.9 cm
Colour:	Tan - gloss
Issued:	1944-c.1963
Set:	1007, 1008
Series:	Fun Models

Description:	U.K. £	U.S. $	Can. $
Gloss	45.00	70.00	100.00

Model No. 1016A
FOX - Standing

Designer:	Arthur Gredington
Height:	5 1/2", 14.0 cm
Colour:	Red-brown and white - gloss or matt
Issued:	1: Gloss - 1945 to the present
	2: Matt - 1985-1988
Varieties:	1016B

Description:	U.K. £	U.S. $	Can. $
1: Gloss	19.95	N/A	N/A
2: Matt	30.00	50.00	75.00

Model No. 1016B
FOX - Standing - on wooden plinth

Designer:	Arthur Gredington
Height:	6 3/4", 17.2 cm
Colour:	Natural - gloss
Issued:	1993 to the present
Varieties:	1016A

Description:	U.K. £	U.S. $	Can. $
Gloss	24.95	N/A	N/A

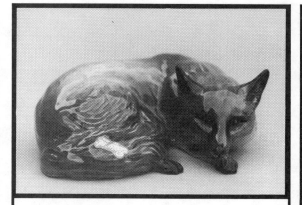

Model No. 1017
FOX - Curled

Designer:	Arthur Gredington
Height:	1 3/4", 3.2 cm
Colour:	Red brown - gloss or matt
Issued:	1: Gloss - 1945 to the present
	2: Matt - 1985-1988

Description:	U.K. £	U.S. $	Can. $
1: Gloss	12.95	N/A	N/A
2: Matt	45.00	70.00	100.00

Model No. 1019
BISON

Designer:	Arthur Gredington
Height:	5 3/4", 14.6 cm
Colour:	Dark brown - gloss
Issued:	1945-1973

Description:	U.K. £	U.S. $	Can. $
Gloss	85.00	135.00	190.00

Model No. 1021
STOAT

Designer:	Arthur Gredington
Height:	5 1/2", 14.0 cm
Colour:	1: Tan (summer coat) - gloss
	2: White (winter coat) - gloss
Issued:	1945-1963

Description:	U.K. £	U.S. $	Can. $
1: Tan	150.00	240.00	335.00
2: White	150.00	240.00	335.00

Model No. 1024
HARE - Running

Designer:	Arthur Gredington
Height:	5 1/4", 12.7 cm
Colour:	Tan - gloss
Issued:	1945-1963

Description:	U.K. £	U.S. $	Can. $
Gloss	150.00	240.00	335.00

Model No. 1025
HARE - Seated

Designer:	Arthur Gredington
Height:	7", 17.8 cm
Colour:	Tan - gloss
Issued:	1945-1963

Description:	U.K. £	U.S. $	Can. $
Gloss	125.00	200.00	275.00

Model No. 1038
KOALA BEAR

Designer:	Arthur Gredington
Height:	3 1/2", 8.9 cm
Colour:	Grey - gloss
Issued:	1945-1971
Set:	1039, 1040

Description:	U.K. £	U.S. $	Can. $
Gloss	35.00	55.00	75.00

Model No. 1039
KOALA BEAR

Designer:	Arthur Gredington
Height:	2 1/4", 5.7 cm
Colour:	Grey - gloss
Issued:	1945-1973
Set:	1038, 1040

Description:	U.K. £	U.S. $	Can. $
Gloss	35.00	55.00	75.00

Model No. 1040
KOALA BEAR

Designer:	Arthur Gredington
Height:	2 1/4", 5.7 cm
Colour:	Grey - gloss
Issued:	1945-1973
Set:	1038, 1039

Description:	U.K. £	U.S. $	Can. $
Gloss	35.00	55.00	75.00

Model No. 1043
CAMEL FOAL

Designer:	Arthur Gredington
Height:	5", 12.7 cm
Colour:	Light and dark brown - gloss
Issued:	1946-1971
Set:	1044

Description:	U.K. £	U.S. $	Can. $
Gloss	110.00	175.00	250.00

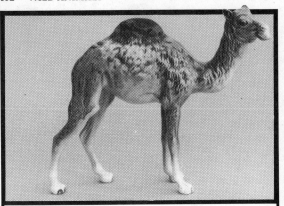

Model No. 1044
CAMEL

Designer:	Arthur Gredington
Height:	7", 17.8 cm
Colour:	Light and dark brown - gloss
Issued:	1946-1973
Set:	1043

Description:	U.K. £	U.S. $	Can. $
Gloss	125.00	200.00	275.00

Model No. 1048
SPRINGBOK

Designer:	Arthur Gredington
Height:	7 1/4", 18.4 cm
Colour:	Tan and white - gloss
Issued:	1946-1963

Description:	U.K. £	U.S. $	Can. $
Gloss	200.00	325.00	450.00

Model No. 1049
CHIMPANZEE WITH PIPE

Designer:	Arthur Gredington
Height:	4 3/4", 12.1 cm
Colour:	Brown - gloss
Issued:	1946-1969

Description:	U.K. £	U.S. $	Can. $
Gloss	125.00	200.00	275.00

Model No. 1082
LEOPARD

Designer:	Arthur Gredington
Height:	4 3/4", 12.1 cm
Colour:	Golden brown with black markings - gloss
Issued:	1946-1975

Description:.	U.K. £	U.S. $	Can. $
Gloss	145.00	225.00	300.00

Model No. 1089
KOALA BEAR

Designer:	Miss Jones
Height:	3 1/2", 8.9 cm
Colour:	Grey - gloss
Issued:	1947-1971

Description:	U.K. £	U.S. $	Can. $
Gloss	35.00	55.00	75.00

Model No. 1160
KANGAROO

Designer:	Arthur Gredington
Height:	5 3/4", 14.6 cm
Colour:	Brown - gloss
Issued:	1949-1966

Description:	U.K. £	U.S. $	Can. $
Gloss	125.00	200.00	275.00

Model No. 1255
MONKEY WITH DRUM

Designer:	Miss Granoska
Height:	2 1/2", 6.4 cm
Colour:	Brown and green - gloss
Issued:	1952-1963
Set:	1256, 1257, 1258, 1259, 1260

Price	U.K. £	U.S. $	Can. $
Gloss	125.00	200.00	275.00

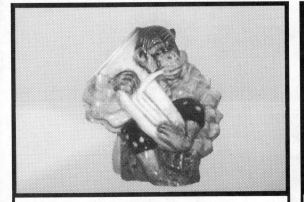

Model No. 1256
MONKEY WITH TUBA

Designer:	Miss Granoska
Height:	2 1/2", 64 cm
Colour:	Brown and green - gloss
Issued:	1952-1963
Set:	1255, 1257, 1258, 1259, 1260

Description:	U.K. £	U.S. $	Can. $
Gloss	125.00	200.00	275.00

Photograph not
available at press time

Model No. 1257
MONKEY WITH FIDDLE

Designer:	Miss Granoska
Height:	2 1/2", 6.4 cm
Colour:	Brown and green - gloss
Issued:	1952-1963
Set:	1255, 1256, 1258, 1259, 1260

Description:	U.K. £	U.S. $	Can. $
Gloss	125.00	200.00	275.00

Model No. 1258
MONKEY WITH SAXOPHONE

Designer:	Miss Granoska
Height:	2 1/2", 6.4 cm
Colour:	Brown and green- gloss
Issued:	1952-1963
Set:	1255, 1256, 1257, 1259, 1260

Description:	U.K. £	U.S. $	Can. $
Gloss	125.00	200.00	275.00

Model No. 1259
MONKEY WITH GUITAR

Designer:	Miss Granoska
Height:	2 1/2", 6.4 cm
Colour:	Brown and green - gloss
Issued:	1952-1963
Set:	1255, 1256, 1257, 1258, 1260

Description:	U.K. £	U.S. $	Can. $
Gloss	125.00	200.00	275.00

Model No. 1260
MONKEY WITH BANJO

Designer:	Miss Granoska
Height:	2 1/2", 6.4 cm
Colour:	Brown and green - gloss
Issued:	1952-1963
Set:	1255, 1256, 1257, 1258, 1259

Description:	U.K. £	U.S. $	Can. $
Gloss	125.00	200.00	275.00

Model No. 1308
SKUNK

Designer:	Arthur Gredington
Height:	2 3/4", 7.0 cm
Colour:	Black and white - gloss
Issued:	1953-1963
Set:	1309, 1310

Description:	U.K. £	U.S. $	Can. $
Gloss	75.00	125.00	160.00

Model No. 1309
SKUNK

Designer:	Arthur Gredington
Height:	1 1/2", 3.8 cm
Colour:	Black and white - gloss
Issued:	1953-1963
Set:	1308, 1310

Description:	U.K. £	U.S. $	Can. $
Gloss	75.00	125.00	160.00

Model No. 1310
SKUNK

Designer:	Arthur Gredington
Height:	2", 5.0 cm
Colour:	Black and white - gloss
Issued:	1953-1963
Set:	1307, 1309

Description:	U.K. £	U.S. $	Can. $
Gloss	75.00	125.00	160.00

Model No. 1313
BEAR - Standing

Designer:	Arthur Gredington
Height:	2 1/2", 6.4 cm
Colour:	Black or brown - gloss
Issued:	1953-1966
Set:	1314, 1315

Description:	U.K. £	U.S. $	Can. $
1: Black	75.00	125.00	160.00
2: Brown	75.00	125.00	160.00

Model No. 1314
BEAR - On hind legs

Designer:	Arthur Gredington
Height:	4 1/2", 11.9 cm
Colour:	Black or brown - gloss
Issued:	1953-1966
Set:	1313, 1315

Description:	U.K. £	U.S. $	Can. $
1: Black	75.00	125.00	160.00
2: Brown	75.00	125.00	160.00

Model No. 1315
BEAR CUB - Seated

Designer:	Arthur Gredington
Height:	2 1/4", 5.7 cm
Colour:	Black or brown - gloss
Issued:	1953-1966
Set:	1313, 1314

Description:	U.K. £	U.S. $	Can. $
1: Black	45.00	70.00	100.00
2: Brown	45.00	70.00	100.00

Model No. 1335
TORTOISE WITH HAT

Designer:	Miss Granoska
Length:	2 3/4", 7.0 cm
Colour:	Brown - gloss
Issued:	1954-1973
Set:	1336, 1337

Description:	U.K. £	U.S. $	Can. $
Gloss	95.00	150.00	200.00

Model No. 1336
TORTOISE WITH BONNET

Designer:	Miss Granoska
Length:	1 3/4", 4.5 cm
Colour:	Brown - gloss
Issued:	1954-1973
Set:	1335, 1337

Description:	U.K. £	U.S. $	Can. $
Gloss	95.00	150.00	200.00

Model No. 1337
TORTOISE WITH CAP

Designer:	Miss Granoska
Length:	1 3/4", 4.5 cm
Colour:	Brown - gloss
Issued:	1954-1973
Set:	1335, 1336

Description:	U.K. £	U.S. $	Can. $
Gloss	95.00	150.00	200.00

Model No. 1379
BUSH BABY - With mirror

Designer:	Mr. Orwell
Height:	2", 5.0 cm
Colour:	Grey-brown - gloss
Issued:	1955-1966
Set:	1380, 1381

Description:	U.K. £	U.S. $	Can. $
Gloss	65.00	100.00	140.00

Model No. 1380
BUSH BABY - With candlestick

Designer:	Mr. Orwell
Height:	2", 5.0 cm
Colour:	Grey-brown - gloss
Issued:	1955-1966
Set:	1379, 1381

Description:	U.K. £	U.S. $	Can. $
Gloss	65.00	100.00	140.00

Model No. 1381
BUSH BABY - With Book

Designer:	Mr. Orwell
Height:	1 1/2", 3.8 cm
Colour:	Grey-brown - gloss
Issued:	1955-1966
Set:	1379, 1380

Description:	*U.K. £*	*U.S. $*	*Can. $*
Gloss	65.00	100.00	140.00

Model No. 1440
FOX - Standing

Designer:	Arthur Gredington
Height:	2 1/2", 6.4 cm
Colour:	Red-brown and white - gloss or matt
Issued:	Gloss - 1956 to the present
	Matt - 1985-1988

Description:	*U.K. £*	*U.S. $*	*Can. $*
1: Gloss	9.95	N/A	N/A
2: Matt	15.00	25.00	35.00

Model No. 1486
TIGERESS

Designer:	Colin Melbourne
Height:	4 1/4", 10.8 cm
Colour:	Tan with black stripes and markings - gloss
Issued:	1957-1975

Description:	*U.K. £*	*U.S. $*	*Can. $*
Gloss	125.00	200.00	295.00

Model No. 1506
LION - Facing right

Designer:	Colin Melbourne
Height:	5 1/4", 13.3 cm
Colour:	Golden brown - gloss
Issued:	1957-1967
Set:	1507, 1508

Description:	*U.K. £*	*U.S. $*	*Can. $*
Gloss	145.00	225.00	300.00

Model No. 1507
LIONESS - Facing left

Designer:	Colin Melbourne
Height:	4 3/4", 12.1 cm
Colour:	Golden brown - gloss
Issued:	1957-1967
Set:	1506, 1508

Description:	U.K. £	U.S. $	Can. $
Gloss	110.00	175.00	240.00

Model No. 1508
LION CUB - Facing right

Designer:	Colin Melbourne
Height:	4", 10.1 cm
Colour:	Golden brown - gloss
Issued:	1957-1967
Set:	1506, 1507

Description:	U.K. £	U.S. $	Can. $
Gloss	110.00	175.00	240.00

Model No. 1532
HIPPOPOTAMUS

Designer:	Colin Melbourne
Height:	3 1/2", 8.9 cm
Colour:	Dark grey with pink underneath - gloss
Issued:	1958-1966

Description:	U.K. £	U.S. $	Can. $
Gloss	125.00	200.00	300.00

Model No. 1533
POLAR BEAR

Designer:	Arthur Gredington
Height:	4 3/4", 12.1 cm
Colour:	White - gloss
Issued:	1958-1966

Description:	U.K. £	U.S. $	Can. $
Gloss	125.00	200.00	300.00

Model No. 1534
SEAL

Designer:	Arthur Gredington
Length:	5 3/4", 14.6 cm
Colour:	Grey - gloss
Issued:	1958-1966

Description:	U.K. £	U.S. $	Can. $
Gloss	125.00	200.00	275.00

Model No. 1551
CHAMOIS

Designer:	Pal Zalmen
Height:	4", 10.1 cm
Colour:	Fawn or grey - gloss
Issued:	1958-1971
Series:	Fun Models

Description:	U.K. £	U.S. $	Can. $
1: Fawn	45.00	70.00	100.00
2: Grey	45.00	70.00	100.00

Model No. 1597
GIRAFFE

Designer:	J. Lawson
Height:	4 1/4", 10.8 cm
Colour:	Tan with dark patches - gloss
Issued:	1959-1971
Series:	Fun Models

Description:	U.K. £	U.S. $	Can. $
Gloss	75.00	120.00	165.00

Model No. 1615
BABYCHAM

Designer:	Albert Hallam
Height:	4", 10.1 cm
Colour:	Yellow - gloss
Issued:	1960-1975
Series:	Fun Models

Description:	U.K. £	U.S. $	Can. $
Gloss	60.00	95.00	135.00

Model No. 1631
GIRAFFE

Designer: J. Lawson
Height: 12", 30.5 cm
Colour: Light brown with dark brown
             patches - gloss
Issued: 1959-1975

Description:	U.K. £	U.S. $	Can. $
Gloss	195.00	300.00	400.00

Model No. 1678
MOUSE

Designer: Albert Hallam
Height: 2 1/2", 6.4 cm
Colour: Grey - gloss
Issued: 1960 to the present

Description:	U.K. £	U.S. $	Can. $
Gloss	5.95	N/A	N/A

Model No. 1688
REINDEER

Designer: J. Lawson
Height: 3 3/4", 9.5 cm
Colour: Fawn or grey - gloss
Issued: 1960-1971
Series: Fun Models

Description:	U.K. £	U.S. $	Can. $
1: Fawn	55.00	85.00	125.00
2: Grey	55.00	85.00	125.00

Model No. 1702
PUMA ON ROCK

Designer:	Arthur Gredington
Height:	8 1/2", 21.6 cm
Colour:	1: Black - gloss
	2: Tawny - gloss or matt
Issued:	1: Black
	A: Gloss - 1960-1973
Re-issued:	B: Gloss - 1979-1983
Issued:	2: Tawny
	A: Gloss - 1960-1975
	B: Matt - 1970-1973
	C: Satin matt - 1973-1989
Re-issued:	D: Tawny gloss - 1979-1983
Series:	Connoisseur Series, 2C

Description:	U.K. £	U.S. $	Can. $
1: Black			
A: Gloss	165.00	250.00	350.00
B: Re-issued	165.00	250.00	350.00
2 Tawny			
A: Gloss	165.00	250.00	350.00
B: Matt	225.00	250.00	350.00
C: Satin matt	145.00	210.00	300.00
D: Re-issued	175.00	210.00	300.00

Model No. 1720
ELEPHANT AND TIGER

Designer:	Arthur Gredington
Height:	12", 30.5 cm
Colour:	Grey, tan with black stripes - gloss
Issued:	1960-1975

Description:	U.K. £	U.S. $	Can. $
Gloss	375.00	600.00	750.00

Note: Elephant same as used in 1770.

Model No. 1733
COMICAL FOX

Designer:	Harry Sales
Height:	3 1/4", 8.3 cm
Colour:	Red-brown and white - gloss
Issued:	1961-1968
Series:	Fun Models

Price	U.K. £	U.S. $	Can. $
Gloss	75.00	125.00	165.00

Model No. 1748
FOX - Seated

Designer:	Arthur Gredington		
Height:	3", 7.6 cm		
Colour:	Red-brown and white - gloss or matt		
Issued:	1: Gloss - 1961 to the present		
	2: Matt - 1985-1988		

Description:	U.K. £	U.S. $	Can. $
1: Gloss	9.95	N/A	N/A
2: Matt	15.00	25.00	35.00

Model No. 1761
FOXY BANK

Designer:	Albert Hallam		
Height:	8 1/2", 21.6 cm		
Colour:	Tan, brown and black on white - gloss		
Issued:	1961-1967		
Series:	Fun Models / Money bank		

Price	U.K. £	U.S. $	Can. $
Various	75.00	125.00	165.00

Model No. 1770
ELEPHANT - Trunk in salute

Designer:	Arthur Gredington		
Height:	12", 30.5 cm		
Colour:	Grey - gloss or satin matt		
Issued:	1: Gloss - 1961-1975		
	2: Satin matt - 1970-1973		

Description:	U.K. £	U.S. $	Can. $
1: Gloss	350.00	550.00	700.00
2: Satin matt	350.00	550.00	700.00

Note: Satin matt transferred to Connoiseur Series in 1973. Elephant same as used in 1720.

Model No. 1815
PANDA BEAR

Designer:	Albert Hallam		
Height:	2 1/4", 5.7 cm		
Colour:	Black and white - gloss or matt		
Issued:	1: Gloss - 1962 to the present		
	2: Matt - 1985-1988		

Description:	U.K. £	U.S. $	Can. $
1: Gloss	7.95	N/A	N/A
2: Matt	15.00	25.00	35.00

Model No. 1823
PUMA ON ROCK

Designer: Arthur Gredington
Height: 6", 15.0 cm
Colour: Black or tawny - gloss
Issued: 1: Black - 1962-1973
  2: Tawny - 1962-1975

Description:	U.K. £	U.S. $	Can. $
1: Black	120.00	190.00	225.00
2: Tawny	120.00	190.00	225.00

Model No. 1943
BEAVER ON LOG - Facing left

Designer: Albert Hallam
Height: 2 1/2", 6.4 cm
Colour: Tan - gloss
Issued: 1964-1967

Description:	U.K. £	U.S. $	Can. $
Gloss	100.00	160.00	225.00

Model No. 2089
LION - Facing left

Designer: Graham Tongue
Height: 5 1/2", 14.0 cm
Colour: Golden brown - gloss
Issued: 1967-1984

Description:	U.K. £	U.S. $	Can. $
Gloss	75.00	125.00	165.00

Model No. 2090
MOOSE

Designer: Arthur Gredington
Height: 6 1/4", 15.9 cm
Colour: Dark brown - gloss or satin matt
Issued: 1967-1973

Description:	U.K. £	U.S. $	Can. $
1: Gloss	250.00	375.00	500.00
2: Satin matt	250.00	375.00	500.00

Model No. 2096
TIGER

Designer:	Graham Tongue
Height:	7 1/2", 19.1 cm
Colour:	Tan with black stripes - gloss or matt
Issued:	1: Gloss - 1967-1990
	2: Matt - 1985-1988

Description:	U.K. £	U.S. $	Can. $
1: Gloss	95.00	150.00	200.00
2: Matt	95.00	150.00	200.00

Model No. 2097
LIONESS - Facing right

Designer:	Colin Melbourne
Height:	5 3/4", 14.6 cm
Colour:	Golden brown - gloss
Issued:	1967-1984

Description:	U.K. £	U.S. $	Can. $
Gloss	110.00	170.00	225.00

Model No. 2098
LION CUB - Facing left

Designer:	Colin Melbourne
Height:	4", 10.1 cm
Colour:	Golden brown - gloss
Issued:	1967-1984

Description:	U.K. £	U.S. $	Can. $
Gloss	65.00	100.00	140.00

Model No. 2131
RABBIT

Designer:	Albert Hallam, Graham Tongue
Height:	3", 7.6 cm
Colour:	Light brown and white - gloss
Issued:	1967-1973
Series:	Fun Models

Description:	U.K. £	U.S. $	Can. $
Gloss	85.00	135.00	175.00

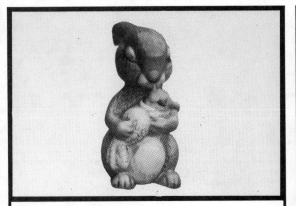

Model No. 2132
RABBIT WITH BABY

Designer:	Albert Hallam
Height:	3", 7.6 cm
Colour:	Light brown and white - gloss
Issued:	1967-1971
Series:	Fun Models

Description:	U.K. £	U.S. $	Can. $
Gloss	85.00	135.00	175.00

Model No. 2194
RACOON ON LOG

Designer:	Albert Hallam
Height:	4 1/4", 10.8 cm
Colour:	Dark grey - gloss
Issued:	1968-1972

Description:	U.K. £	U.S. $	Can. $
Gloss	150.00	240.00	335.00

Model No. 2195
BEAVER ON LOG - Facing right

Designer:	Albert Hallam
Height:	4 1/2", 11.9 cm
Colour:	Brown - gloss
Issued:	1968-c.1973

Description:	U.K. £	U.S. $	Can. $
Gloss	150.00	240.00	335.00

Photograph not
available at press time

Model No. 2253
HEDGEHOG

Designer:	Harry Sales
Height:	3 1/2" 8.9 cm
Colour:	1: Blue - gloss
	2: Brown - gloss
Issued:	1969-1971
Series:	Moda Range

Description:	U.K. £	U.S. $	Can. $
1: Brown	100.00	150.00	225.00
2: Blue	100.00	150.00	225.00

Photograph not
available at press time

Model No. 2302
MOUSE

Designer: Albert Hallam
Height: 1 3/4", 8.9 cm
Colour: Unknown
Issued: 1969-Unknown

Description:	*U.K. £*	*U.S. $*	*Can. $*
		Possibly not put into production.	

Model No. 2312
KANGAROO

Designer: Albert Hallam
Height: 5", 12.7 cm
Colour: Light and dark brown - gloss
Issued: 1970-1973

Description:	*U.K. £*	*U.S. $*	*Can. $*
Gloss	125.00	200.00	250.00

Model No. 2348
FOX

Designer: Graham Tongue
Height: 12 1/2", 31.7 cm
Colour: Red-brown and white - gloss
Issued: 1970-1984
Series: Fireside Model

Description:	*U.K. £*	*U.S. $*	*Can. $*
Gloss	195.00	300.00	375.00

Model No. 2554A
LION ON ROCK

Designer: Graham Tongue
Height: 8 1/4", 21.0 cm
Colour: Golden brown - satin matt
Issued: 1975-1984
Varieties: 2554B (standing)
Series: Connoisseur

Description:	*U.K. £*	*U.S. $*	*Can. $*
Satin matt	195.00	300.00	375.00

Model No. 2554B
LION - Standing

Designer:	Graham Tongue
Height:	6 3/4", 17.2 cm
Colour:	Golden brown - gloss
Modelled:	1975
Issued:	1987-1995

Description:	*U.K. £*	*U.S. $*	*Can. $*
Gloss	195.00	300.00	375.00

Model No. 2613
PANDA "CHI CHI"
Version One - With bamboo shoot

Designer:	Unknown
Height:	3 3/4", 9.5 cm
Colour:	Black and white - gloss
Issued:	1978-c.1980
Varieties:	2944

Description:	*U.K. £*	*U.S. $*	*Can. $*
Gloss	75.00	110.00	150.00

Note: This model was produced for the London Natural History Museum.

Model No. 2629
STAG

Designer:	Graham Tongue
Height:	13 1/2", 34.3 cm
Colour:	Golden brown - satin matt
Issued:	1978-1989
Series:	Connoisseur

Description:	*U.K. £*	*U.S. $*	*Can. $*
Satin matt	150.00	250.00	350.00

Note: Transferred to R.D. backstamp (DA 32), 08/89, later called "The Majestic Stag".

Model No. 2686
OTTER

Designer:	David Lyttleton
Height:	2 1/4", 5.7 cm
Colour:	Grey - matt
Issued:	1985-1985

Description:	*U.K. £*	*U.S. $*	*Can. $*
Matt		Rare	

Note: Part of a trial run in 1985 but never put into general production.

Model No. 2687
BADGER

Designer:	David Lyttleton
Height:	3", 7.6 cm
Colour:	Black - matt
Issued:	1985-1985

Description:	U.K. £	U.S. $	Can. $
Matt		Rare	

Note: Part of a trial run in 1985 but never put into general production.

Model No. 2693
SEAL

Designer:	Graham Tongue
Height:	3 1/2", 8.9 cm
Colour:	Grey - matt
Issued:	1985-1985

Description:	U.K. £	U.S. $	Can. $
Matt		Rare	

Note: Part of a trial run in 1985 but never put into general production.

Model No. 2725
CHEETAH ON ROCK

Designer:	Graham Tongue
Height:	6 1/2", 16.5 cm
Colour:	Pale brown with dark spots - satin finish
Issued:	1981-1989
Series:	Connoisseur

Description:	U.K. £	U.S. $	Can. $
Satin finish	175.00	275.00	400.00

Note: Transferred to R.D. backstamp (DA 39) 08/89 later called "The Watering Hole"

Model No. 2944
PANDA BEAR "CHI CHI"
Version Two - Without bamboo shoot

Designer:	Unknown
Height:	3 3/4", 9.5 cm
Colour:	Black and white - matt
Issued:	1985-1985
Varieties:	2613

Description:	U.K. £	U.S. $	Can. $
Matt		Rare	

Note: Part of a trial run in 1985 but did not go into general production.

Model No. 3009
CHEETAH - Standing

Designer:	Graham Tongue
Height:	5", 12.7 cm
Colour:	Golden brown with dark spots - gloss
Issued:	1986-1995

Description:	U.K. £	U.S. $	Can. $
Gloss	40.00	70.00	90.00

Model No. 3392
BADGER CUB

Designer:	Amanda Hughes-Lubeck
Height:	2", 5.0 cm
Colour:	Black and white - gloss
Issued:	1992 to the present
Set:	3393, 3394

Description:	U.K. £	U.S. $	Can. $
Gloss	9.95	N/A	N/A

Model No. 3393
BADGER - Male

Designer:	Amanda Hughes-Lubeck
Height:	2", 5.0 cm
Colour:	Black and white - gloss
Issued:	1992 to the present
Set:	3392, 3394

Description:	U.K. £	U.S. $	Can. $
Gloss	12.95	N/A	N/A

Model No. 3394
BADGER - Female

Designer:	Amanda Hughes-Lubeck
Height:	2", 5.0 cm
Colour:	Black and white - gloss
Issued:	1992 to the present
Set:	3392, 3393

Description:	U.K. £	U.S. $	Can. $
Gloss	12.95	N/A	N/A

Model No. 3397
HARVEST MOUSE

Designer:	Martyn C.R. Alcock
Height:	2 1/4", 5.7 cm
Colour:	Brown - gloss
Issued:	1992 to the present

Description:	U.K. £	U.S. $	Can. $
Gloss	9.95	30.00	35.00

Model No. 3399
WOODMOUSE

Designer:	Martyn C. R. Alcock
Height:	3 1/4", 8.3 cm
Colour:	Brown - gloss
Issued:	1992 to the present

Description:	U.K. £	U.S. $	Can. $
Goss	9.95	26.00	35.00

WILD ANIMAL
WALL PLAQUES

Model No. 2933
LION'S HEAD

Designer: Graham Tongue
Height: 6", 15.0 cm
Colour: Golden brown - matt
Issued: 1985-1989

Description:	U.K. £	U.S. $	Can. $
Matt	65.00	95.00	125.00

Model No. 2934
TIGER'S HEAD

Designer: Arthur Gredington
Height: 6", 15.0 cm
Colour: Tan - matt
Issued: 1985-1989

Description:	U.K. £	U.S. $	Can. $
Matt	65.00	95.00	125.00

Model No. 2936
STAG'S HEAD

Designer: Graham Tongue
Height: 6", 15.0 cm
Colour: Light brown - matt
Issued: 1985-1989

Description:	U.K. £	U.S. $	Can. $
Matt	65.00	95.00	125.00

Chapter Nine

THE CM SERIES

This unique series of models, all created by Colin Melbourne, evokes great emotion amongst collectors; it is either loved or disliked. No half measures here.

The models were called "contemporary" when they were in production during the late 1950s. They reflected the mood of the time, both in style and in decoration. None of the decorations are realistic, and all are stylized, some to a greater extent than others.

The decoration falls into two main categories . The so-called chalk design is a white background colour on which various geometric shapes or floral designs appear. The designs are in a variety of colours, the most common being red, brown, blue and yellow.

The other main form of decoration is the use of a solid colour, such as brown or blue, with the addition of lines or blocks of another colour, such as red on a brown background with perhaps a touch of black.

We wish to thank Royal Doulton for providing some of the illustrations in this section.

INDEX BY MODEL NUMBER

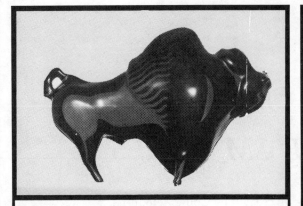

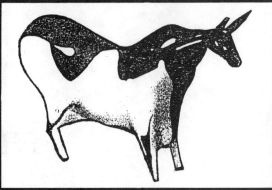

Model No. 1409
BISON - Large

Designer:	Colin Melbourne
Length:	7 1/2" x 10 1/2", 19.1 x 26.7 cm
Colour:	Chalk on solid colours - satin
Issued:	1956-By 1963

Description:	U.K. £	U.S. $	Can. $
Satin	140.00	225.00	300.00

Model No. 1410
COW

Designer:	Colin Melbourne
Height:	5", 12.7 cm
Colour:	Black and white - satin
Issued:	1956-By 1963

Description:	U.K. £	U.S. $	Can. $
Satin	135.00	225.00	300.00

Model No. 1411
HORSE

Designer:	Colin Melbourne
Height:	8 1/2", 21,6 cm
Colour:	1: Solid colour - satin
	2: Brown and black - satin
	3: Patterned - satin
Issued:	1956-By 1966

Description:	U.K. £	U.S. $	Can. $
1: Solid colour	120.00	190.00	275.00
2: Two-colours	180.00	275.00	400.00
3: Patterned	200.00	325.00	450.00

Model No. 1412
CAT - Large

Designer:	Colin Melbourne
Height:	9 1/2", 24.0 cm
Colour:	Chalk base with spots, geometric lines
	or flowers - satin
Issued:	1956-By 1966

Description:	U.K. £	U.S. $	Can. $
Satin	145.00	225.00	325.00

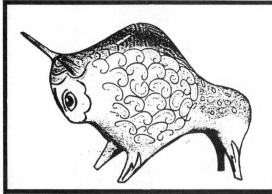

Model No. 1413
DOVE

Designer:	Colin Melbourne
Height:	9", 22.9 cm
Colour:	Various - satin
Issued:	1956-By 1965

Description:	U.K. £	U.S. $	Can. $
Satin	110.00	175.00	250.00

Model No. 1414
BISON - Small

Designer:	Colin Melbourne
Length:	5 1/2" x 8 3/4", 14.0 x 22.2 cm
Colour:	Various - satin
Issued:	1956-By 1966

Description:	U.K. £	U.S. $	Can. $
Satin	120.00	195.00	275.00

Model No. 1415
BIRD

Designer:	Colin Melbourne
Height:	5 1/4", 13.3 cm
Colour:	Various - satin
Issued:	1956-By 1965

Description:	U.K. £	U.S. $	Can. $
Satin	110.00	175.00	250.00

Model No. 1416
COCK - Small

Designer:	Colin Melbourne
Height:	5", 12.7 cm
Colour:	Various - satin
Issued:	1956-By 1965

Description:	U.K. £	U.S. $	Can. $
Satin	120.00	195.00	275.00

Model No. 1417
CAT - Small

Designer:	Colin Melbourne
Height:	5 1/2", 14.0 cm
Colour:	Chalk base with spots, geometric lines or flowers - satin
Issued:	1956-By 1966

Description:	U.K. £	U.S. $	Can. $
Satin	145.00	225.00	325.00

Model No. 1418
FOX - Small

Designer:	Colin Melbourne
Length:	2" x 8", 5.0 x 20.3 cm
Colour:	Various - satin
Issued:	1956-By 1966

Description:	U.K. £	U.S. $	Can. $
Satin	125.00	200.00	275.00

Photograph not
available at press time

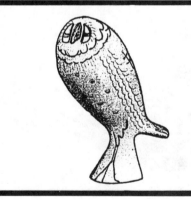

Model No. 1419
LION

Designer:	Colin Melbourne
Height:	4 3/4", 12.1 cm
Colour:	Various - satin
Issued:	1956-By 1963

Description:	U.K. £	U.S. $	Can. $
Satin	150.00	250.00	325.00

Model No. 1420
OWL - Small

Designer:	Colin Melbourne
Height:	4 3/4", 12.1 cm
Colour:	Various - satin
Issued:	1956-By 1965

Description:	U.K. £	U.S. $	Can. $
Satin	135.00	225.00	300.00

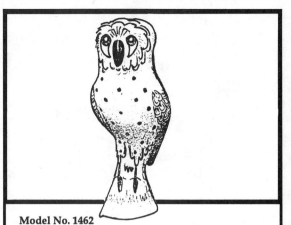

Model No. 1462
OWL - Large

Designer:	Colin Melbourne
Height:	8 1/4", 21.0 cm
Colour:	Various - satin
Issued:	1956-By 1965

Description:	U.K. £	U.S. $	Can. $
Satin	165.00	265.00	1375.00

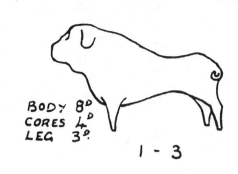

Model No. 1463
BULLDOG

Designer:	Colin Melbourne
Height:	Unknown
Colour:	Various - satin
Issued:	1956-1970

Description:	U.K. £	U.S. $	Can. $
Satin	6175.00	275.00	395.00

Model No. 1465
ZEBRA

Designer:	Colin Melbourne
Height:	6", 15.0 cm
Colour:	Black and white - satin
Issued:	1956-By 1966

Description:	U.K. £	U.S. $	Can. $
Satin	125.00	200.00	275.00

Model No. 1467
COCK - Large

Designer:	Colin Melbourne
Height:	11 3/4", 29.8 cm
Colour:	Various - satin
Issued:	1956-By 1963

Description:	U.K. £	U.S. $	Can. $
Satin	185.00	295.00	400.00

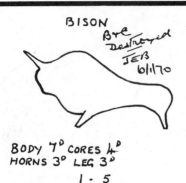

Model No. 1468
BISON

Designer:	Colin Melbourne
Height:	Unknown
Colour:	Various - satin
Issued:	1956-By 1966

Description:	*U.K. £*	*U.S. $*	*Can. $*
Satin		Extremely Rare	

Model No. 1469
DACHSHUND

Designer:	Colin Melbourne
Length:	7", 17.8 cm
Colour:	Various - satin
Issued:	1957-1970

Description:	*U.K. £*	*U.S. $*	*Can. $*
Satin	145.00	225.00	325.00

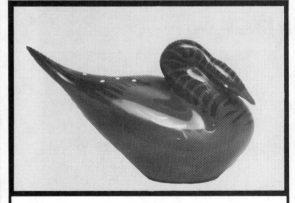

Model No. 1470
CLOWN ON HORSE - Small

Designer:	Colin Melbourne
Height:	5 3/4", 14.6 cm
Colour:	Various - satin
Issued:	1957-By 1966

Description:	*U.K. £*	*U.S. $*	*Can. $*
Satin	145.00	225.00	325.00

Model No. 1471
GOOSE

Designer:	Colin Melbourne
Height:	3 1/2", 8.9 cm
Colour:	Various - satin
Issued:	1957-By 1962

Description:	*U.K. £*	*U.S. $*	*Can. $*
Satin	125.00	200.00	275.00

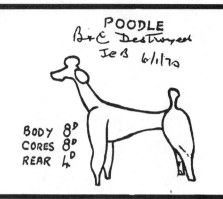

Model No. 1472
POODLE

Designer:	Colin Melbourne
Height:	6 3/4", 17.2 cm
Colour:	Various - satin
Issued:	1957-1970

Description:	U.K. £	U.S. $	Can. $
Satin	135.00	225.00	300.00

Model No. 1473
PIG

Designer:	Colin Melbourne
Length:	2 1/2" x 6", 6.4 x 15.0 cm
Colour:	Various - satin
Issued:	1957-By 1965

Description:	U.K. £	U.S. $	Can. $
Satin	110.00	175.00	250.00

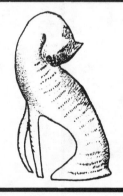

Model No. 1474
CAT

Designer:	Colin Melbourne
Height:	5 1/4", 13.3 cm
Colour:	Chalk base with spots, geometric lines or flowers - satin
Issued:	1957-By 1966

Description:	U.K. £	U.S. $	Can. $
Satin	145.00	225.00	325.00

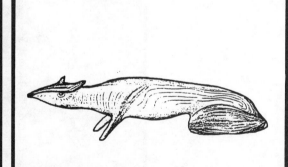

Model No. 1475
FOX - Large

Designer:	Colin Melbourne
Length:	10 1/2", 26.7 cm
Colour:	Various - satin
Issued:	1957-By 1966

Description:	U.K. £	U.S. $	Can. $
Satin	175.00	275.00	400.00

Model No. 1476
CLOWN ON HORSE - Large

Designer:	Colin Melbourne
Height:	8 1/2", 21.6 cm
Colour:	Charcoal grey - satin
Issued:	1957-By 1966

Description:	U.K. £	U.S. $	Can. $
Satin	165.00	265.00	375.00

Model No. 1481
REINDEER

Designer:	Colin Melbourne
Height:	5 1/2", 14.0 cm
Colour:	Various - satin
Issued:	1957-By 1966

Description:	U.K. £	U.S. $	Can. $
Satin	175.00	275.00	400.00

Model No. 1482
PEACOCK

Designer:	Colin Melbourne
Height:	3 1/2", 8.9 cm
Colour:	Various - satin
Issued:	1957-By 1965

Description:	U.K. £	U.S. $	Can. $
Satin	145.00	225.00	325.00

Chapter Ten
STUDIO SCULPTURES

The series of Studio Sculptures made a very brief appearance, most for a maximum of two years, and some for only six months, between 1984 and 1985. When the collection was launched, Harry Sales, Beswick's Design Manager, explained "The new bonded ceramic body gives us endless oportunities to capture every minute detail of the subject and bring the sculptures to life."

The models in this new medium formed four groups, of which two are relevant to this book. These are: the "Countryside Series" which consists of fourteen models and includes birds, a squirrel, dogs, and rabbits, and the "Young Friends Series" which contained four different models, two of which are in two colourways, of pet cats and dogs. None of the models were "free standing" for the model incorporated a base, and some had an additional wooden plinth.

The Studio Sculptures were completely different in style and detail because of the different medium used. They were also different in price! In 1985 their prices ranged from £13.95 to £59.00 and they were considerably more than models in earthenware. For example the Studio Sculpture Wren "Early Bird" retailed at £15.95 whilst the Beswick Wren (993) was £4.95 quite a difference. Therefore it was not too surprising to find that overall the series was not the expected commercial success and so it was not listed in the 1986 price list.

INDEX BY MODEL NUMBER

For other figurines in the Studio Sculpture Series see The Charlton Standard Catalogue of Royal Doulton Beswick Storybook Figurines.

Beatrix Potter Series- SS1, SS2, SS3, SS4, SS11, SS26, SS27

Thelwell Series - SS7, SS12; SS23-25 not allocated.

SS5
PUPPY LOVE (Two puppies)

Designer:	Unknown
Height:	4 1/2", 11.9 cm
Colour:	1: One brown/white, one black/white - Satin matt
	2: One black/white, one white with black patches - satin matt
Issued:	1984-1986
Series:	Young Friends

Description:	U.K. £	U.S. $	Can. $
1: Brown/white	65.00	100.00	125.00
2: Black/white	65.00	100.00	125.00

SS6
I SPY (Two kittens)

Designer:	Unknown
Height:	4 1/2", 11.9 cm
Colour:	1: Two white cats - satin matt
	2: One tabby, one ginger - satin matt
Issued:	1984-1986
Series:	Young Friends

Description:	U.K. £	U.S. $	Can. $
1: White	65.00	100.00	125.00
2: Tabby/ginger	65.00	100.00	125.00

SS8
CONTENTMENT
(Dutch Rabbits)

Designer:	Unknown
Length:	4 3/4", 12.1 cm
Colour:	1: Brown and white - satin matt
	2: Black and white - satin matt
Issued:	1984-1986
Series:	Countryside

Description:	U.K. £	U.S. $	Can. $
1: Brown/white	55.00	80.00	100.00
2: Black/white	55.00	80.00	100.00

SS9
BRIGHT EYES
(Dutch Rabbit)

Designer:	Unknown
Length:	4 1/2", 11.9 cm
Colour:	1: Brown and white - satin matt
	2: Black and white - satin matt
Issued:	1984-1986
Series:	Countryside

Description:	U.K. £	U.S. $	Can. $
1: Brown/white	45.00	70.00	90.00
2: Black/white	45.00	70.00	90.00

SS10
MIND HOW YOU GO
(Goose and goslings)

Designer:	Unknown
Length:	5 1/4", 13.3 cm
Colour:	White goose and yellow goslings - satin matt
Issued:	1984-1986
Series:	Countryside

Description:	U.K. £	U.S. $	Can. $
Satin matt	50.00	75.00	100.00

SS13
HAPPY LANDINGS
(Swan on wooden base)

Designer:	Unknown
Height:	5", 12.7 cm
Colour:	White - satin matt
Issued:	1984-1986
Series:	Countryside

Description:	U.K. £	U.S. $	Can. $
Satin matt	45.00	70.00	90.00

SS14
THE CHASE
(Dogs on wooden base)

Designer:	Unknown
Height:	4", 10.1 cm
Colour:	Shaded brown and white - satin matt
Issued:	1984-1986
Series:	Countryside

Description:	U.K. £	U.S. $	Can. $
Satin matt	65.00	100.00	125.00

SS15
HIDE AND SEEK
(Dogs on wooden base)

Designer:	Unknown
Height:	4 1/2", 11.9 cm
Colour:	Shaded brown - satin matt
Issued:	1984-1986
Series:	Countryside

Description:	U.K. £	U.S. $	Can. $
Satin matt	65.00	100.00	125.00

SS16
MENU FOR TODAY
(Spaniel puppy with kitten)

Designer:	Unknown
Height:	3 1/2", 8.9 cm
Colour:	1: Brown puppy, white kitten - satin matt
	2: Brown puppy, tabby kitten - satin matt
Issued:	1984-1986
Series:	Young Friends

Description:	U.K. £	U.S. $	Can. $
1: Brown/white	65.00	100.00	125.00
2: Brown/tabby	65.00	100.00	125.00

SS17
SHARING
(German Shepherd puppy with kitten)

Designer:	Unknown
Height:	3 1/2", 8.9 cm
Colour:	Black and brown dog, white kitten - satin matt
Issued:	1984-1986
Series:	Young Friends

Description:	U.K. £	U.S. $	Can. $
Satin matt	65.00	100.00	125.00

SS18
PLANNING AHEAD
(Squirrel)

Designer:	Unknown
Height:	3", 7.6 cm
Colour:	Red - satin matt
Issued:	1984-1986
Series:	Countryside

Description:	U.K. £	U.S. $	Can. $
Satin matt	45.00	70.00	90.00

SS19
EARLY BIRD
(Wren)

Designer:	Unknown
Height:	2 1/2", 6.4 cm
Colour:	Dark and light brown - satin matt
Issued:	1984-1986
Series:	Countryside

Description:	U.K. £	U.S. $	Can. $
Satin matt	45.00	70.00	90.00

Photograph not
available at press time

SS20
GOLDEN RETRIEVER - on wooden base

Designer:	Unknown		
Height:	5", 12.7 cm		
Colour:	Golden brown - satin matt		
Issued:	1984-1986		
Series:	Countryside		

Description:	U.K. £	U.S. $	Can. $
Satin matt	55.00	80.00	100.00

Photograph not
available at press time

SS21
POINTER - on wooden base

Designer:	Unknown		
Height:	5", 12.7 cm		
Colour:	White and brown - satin matt		
Issued:	1984-1986		
Series:	Countryside		

Description:	U.K. £	U.S. $	Can. $
Satin matt	55.00	80.00	100.00

Photograph not
available at press time

SS22
ENGLISH SETTER - on wooden base

Designer:	Unknown		
Height:	5", 12.7 cm		
Colour:	White and liver - satin matt		
Issued:	1984-1986		
Series:	Countryside		

Description:	U.K. £	U.S. $	Can. $
Satin matt	55.00	80.00	100.00

SS28
ROBIN

Designer:	Unknown		
Height:	3", 7.6 cm		
Colour:	Brown and red - satin matt		
Issued:	1985-1986		
Series:	Countryside		

Description:	U.K. £	U.S. $	Can. $
Satin matt	45.00	70.00	90.00

SS29
BLUE TIT

Designer:	Unknown
Height:	2 1/2", 6.4 cm
Colour:	Yellow, green and white - satin matt
Issued:	1985-1986
Series:	Countryside

Description:	U.K. £	U.S. $	Can. $
Satin matt	45.00	70.00	90.00

SS30
CHAFFINCH

Designer:	Unknown
Height:	2 1/4", 5.7 cm
Colour:	Brown, ochre, grey, black - satin matt
Issued:	1985-1986
Series:	Countryside

Description:	U.K. £	U.S. $	Can. $
Satin matt	45.00	70.00	90.00

Chapter Eleven

WHISKY FLASKS

INDEX BY MODEL NUMBER

Model No. 2051
LOCH NESS MONSTER (NESSIE)

Designer:	Albert Hallam
Height:	3", 7.6 cm
Colours:	Grey-green - gloss
Issued:	1965-1986

Description:	U.K. £	U.S. $	Can. $
1: Head stopper	30.00	40.00	50.00
2: Base stopper	20.00	27.50	25.00

Model No. 2104
EAGLE

Designer:	Graham Tongue
Height:	4", 10.1 cm
Colours:	Brown - gloss
Issued:	1967-1986

Description:	U.K. £	U.S. $	Can. $
Gloss	45.00	70.00	90.00

Photograph not
available at press time

Model No. 2281
EAGLE

Designer:	Graham Tongue
Height:	11", 27.9 cm
Colours:	Brown - gloss
Issued:	1969-1984

Description:	U.K. £	U.S. $	Can. $
Gloss	85.00	125.00	175.00

Note: Model no. 2281 was re-modelled in 1980 with
a removable head stopper.

Model No. 2350
HAGGIS BIRD

Designer:	Mr. Haywood
Re-modelled:	Albert Hallam
Height:	2 1/2", 6.4 cm
Colours:	Brown - gloss
Issued:	1971-1986

Description:	U.K. £	U.S. $	Can. $
Gloss	15.00	25.00	30.00

Model No. 2561
GROUSE

Designer:	David Lyttleton
Height:	9", 22.9 cm
Colours:	Brown and red - gloss
Issued:	1976-1984

Description:	U.K. £	U.S. $	Can. $
Gloss	85.00	125.00	175.00

Note: Model no. 2561 was re-modelled with a removable head stopper.

Model No. 2583
OSPREY

Designer:	David Lyttleton
Height:	7 3/4", 19.7 cm
Colours:	Browns and white - gloss
Issued:	1977-1986

Description::	U.K. £	U.S. $	Can. $
Gloss	85.00	125.00	175.00

Model No. 2636
SQUIRREL

Designer:	David Lyttleton
Height:	3 1/2", 8.9 cm
Colour:	Red-brown - gloss
Issued:	1978-1986

Description:	U.K. £	U.S. $	Can. $
Gloss	30.00	45.00	60.00

Model No. 2639
KESTREL

Designer:	Graham Tongue
Height:	6 1/2", 16.5 cm
Colours:	Dark grey and white - gloss
Issued:	1979-1986

Description:	U.K. £	U.S. $	Can. $
Gloss	95.00	150.00	200.00

Model No. 2640
BUZZARD

Designer:	Graham Tongue
Height:	6 1/2", 16.5 cm
Colours:	Dark brown and grey - gloss
Issued:	1979-1986

Description:	U.K. £	U.S. $	Can. $
Gloss	95.00	150.00	20.00

Model No. 2641
MERLIN

Designer:	Graham Tongue
Height:	6 1/2", 16.5 cm
Colours:	Dark grey and white - gloss
Issued:	1979-1986

Description:	U.K. £	U.S. $	Can. $
Gloss	95.00	150.00	200.00

Model No. 2642
PEREGRINE FALCON

Designer:	Graham Tongue
Height:	6 1/2", 16.5 cm
Colours:	Dark grey and white - gloss
Issued:	1979-1986

Description:	U.K. £	U.S. $	Can. $
Gloss	9.00	150.00	200.00

Model No. 2678
EAGLE

Designer:	Graham Tongue
Height:	10 1/2", 26.7 cm
Colours:	Light and dark brown - gloss
Issued:	1980- 1987

Description:	U.K. £	U.S. $	Can. $
Gloss	95.00	150.00	200.00

Model No. 2686
OTTER

Designer:	David Lyttleton
Height:	2 1/4", 5.7 cm
Colour:	Grey and brown - gloss
Issued:	1981-1986

Description:	U.K. £	U.S. $	Can. $
Gloss	15.00	25.00	30.00

Model No. 2687
BADGER

Designer:	David Lyttleton
Height:	3", 7.6 cm
Colour:	Black and white - gloss
Issued:	1981-1986

Description:	U.K. £	U.S. $	Can. $
Gloss	20.00	27.50	35.00

Model No. 2693
SEAL

Designer:	Graham Tongue
Height:	3 1/2", 8.9 cm
Colour:	Grey - gloss
Issued:	1980-1986

Description:	U.K. £	U.S. $	Can. $
Gloss	15.00	25.00	30.00

Model No. 2781
TAWNY OWL

Designer:	Graham Tongue
Height:	6 1/4", 15.9 cm
Colours:	Brown - gloss
Issued:	1982-1987

Description:	U.K. £	U.S. $	Can. $
Gloss	95.00	150.00	200.00

Model No. 2798
GROUSE

Designer:	David Lyttleton
Height:	9 1/2", 24.0 cm
Colours:	Brown and red - matt
Issued:	1982-1987

Description:	U.K. £	U.S. $	Can. $
Gloss	95.00	150.00	200.00

Model No. 2809
BARN OWL

Designer:	Graham Tongue
Height:	6 3/4", 17.2 cm
Colours:	Tan-brown and white - gloss
Issued:	1983-1987

Description:	U.K. £	U.S . $	Can. $
Gloss	95.00	150.00	200.00

Model No. 2825
SHORT EARED OWL

Designer:	Graham Tongue
Height:	6 3/4", 17.2 cm
Colours:	Dark and light brown - gloss
Issued:	1983-1987

Description:	U.K. £	U.S. $	Can. $
Gloss	98.00	125.00	175.00

Model No. 2826
SNOWY OWL

Designer:	Graham Tongue
Height:	1: 6 1/2", 16.5 cm
	2: 5 3/4", 14.6 cm
Colours:	White - gloss
Issued:	1983-1987

Description:	U.K. £	U.S . $	Can. $
1: Large	85.00	125.00	175.00
2: Small	75.00	100.00	150.00

Chapter Twelve

INDICES

INDEX OF MODEL NUMBERS

ALPHABETICAL INDEX

The CHARLTON PRESS

— *NEW BOOKS FOR COLLECTORS* —

1995/1996

PAPER MONEY
The Charlton Standard Catalogue of Canadian Government Paper Money,
8th Edition: $19.95
The Charlton Standard Catalogue of Canadian Chartered Bank Notes
2nd Edition, Hardcover: $49.50

COINS
The 1996 Charlton Coin Guide 35th Edition: $4.95
The Charlton Standard Catalogue of Canadian Coins, 49th Edition: $9.95

TOKENS
The Charlton Standard Catalogue of Canadian Colonial Tokens 2nd Edition: $19.95
The Charlton Canadian Colonial Workbook 1st Edition: $14.95
The Charlton Standard Catalogue of Canadian Communion Tokens 1st Edition: $19.95

MEDALS & BADGES
The Charlton Standard Catalogue of First World War Canadian Infantry Badges,
2nd Edition: $24.95
The Charlton Standard Catalogue of First World War Canadian Corps Badges,
1st Edition: $24.95
The Distinguished Conduct and Military Medal 1st Edition: $19.95
The Distinguished Flying Medal 1st Edition: $19.95

SPORTSCARDS
The Charlton Standard Catalogue of Hockey Cards 6th Edition: $29.95
The Charlton Standard Catalogue of Canadian Baseball and Football Cards
4th Edition: $29.95

ROYAL DOULTON
The Charlton Standard Catalogue of Beswick Animals, 1st Edition: $24.95
The Charlton Standard Catalogue of Royal Doulton Figurines 4th Edition: $24.95
The Charlton Standard Catalogue of Royal Doulton Animals 1st Edition: $24.95
The Charlton Price Guide to Royal Doulton Beswick Storybook Figurines,
2nd Edition: $19.95
The Charlton Standard Catalogue of Royal Doulton Jugs 3rd Edition: $24.95

OTHER BOOKS OF INTEREST TO COLLECTORS
The Charlton Standard Catalogue of Canadian Tire
Cash Bonus Coupons 2nd Edition: $14.95
The 1995 Charlton Collector's Guide to Ontario 5th Edition: $9.95

The CHARLTON PRESS
2010 Yonge Street, Toronto Ontario M4S 1Z9
416-488-4653   Fax 416-488-4656